CHAPTER ONE

My story is a story worth telling. It wasn't just a "flat line." It was a life full of ups and downs. The ups and downs are what I today call life. You know, the deepest and the darkest pain that rips you apart and the highest sweetness of love and joy. Both make you feel alive. Feel that you are there, in the middle of life. After life there just is the "flat line." Or is there something else? Who knows what I could get up to as just a "flat line?"

My name is Mary, Mary Eileen Cooke, or how my friends and family call me "Mollie." So please call me Mollie.

It all started at the beginning of the 20th century. I was born as 1st Price child on a chilly September morning. The year is not important. We all have our little secrets. But it was before the 2nd World War, so much I am prepared to give away. The 2nd World War I was meant to experience very well, but more to that later on in my story. Anyway, I grew up as a country lass near the Welsh-English border with two brothers. The three of us were quite a bundle. We loved to roam and play outdoors. Growing up in the country is a lovely thing for children. We ran up the rural hills, played hide-and-seek in the woods and lay in the long grass letting the wind comb our hair. Coming home late with muddy fingers, the grass strains on our cloths and our sticky hair would always get us into trouble with Mum. But we would consider the trouble worth it in order to be able to spend as much time as possible in our fantasy world in the woods, or on top of the hills.

After school, we ran up the lane squealing and shouting, expecting only the best to come along. My legs were always a little shorter than everybody else's. I really don't know what the Lord was up to when he was making me. So consequently I would be the last to jump into the soft grass on the other side of the cattle grid. My quick and witty humour made up for my shortage of legs, so I never really felt like the loser of a race.

A short but steep hill led up to the wood. Arriving at the entrance of our cool wonderland after defeating the rather large steps that were dug into the hill indicating the path, we were panting and our foreheads glistering with small wet pearls. This is the moment our adventure would start. We stood in front of the great doors to our secret magic kingdom. Feeling dizzy from excitement, paired with a little hidden fear of what or who else could be roaming the wood, we slipped through the gate with wobbly knees. The tall trees protect the spongy footpath from sunlight. Their roots are like spider legs, just much larger and ideal to hide behind. The moss patches between the tall giants are home to ferns that are larger than us. But my favourites are the wild woodland flowers, especially the pink dainty dragonflowers. I would pick one and carefully place it between my blond curls. It wouldn't stay there long. As soon as my brothers caught me doing this, they would chase me and take turns trying to muddle up my hair, leaving me looking like a wild child. My brother John Leslie, or just Les as we called him, excitedly shouts out today's game. It's hide and seek.

The whole wood is the games' territory, and that makes my knees wobble once again. The loser of the race to the cattle grid is first to count. So that's me. The rules are as follows: the counter is the king-tree protector. The king tree is tall and wide and stands in the middle of an open space, surrounded by human-sized ferns that look like the king's personnel. This majestic giant is my counting point and I am his knight in silver armour, protecting him from my brothers, the lumberjacks. Once I spot a lumberjack, I have to race back to my king and touch him first before my enemy can. By doing this, my king is safe and the game is over for the lumberjack.

The game starts. I turn to the king tree, close my eyes and start counting to hundred. 1.2.3.4…

To keep my balance I am kind of cuddling the tree. 9.10.11.12…

The bark is rough and thick, it feels strong, full of life. 20.21.22.23…

At some patches, moss covers the bark making it soft, a home. 30.31.32.33…

Excitement shoots through my legs right up into my tummy. 41.42.43.44…

Nearly half-way, the sound of my brothers' excitement is far away. The cracking of breaking sticks beneath their fast steps has died down. 53.54.55.56…

Holding on to the tree, I believe I can feel his life energy rushing through his veins. It feels powerful, full of ancient knowledge. 60.61.62.63...

My thoughts start to drift off. I feel as though the tree's energy is soaking into my body, taking me to faraway places. 69.70.71.72...

My silver shining armour is becoming stronger with every count. 79.80.81.82...

Something scurries across my fingers, and I jump back into the 20th century, nearly screaming. But I am not allowed to open my eyes before reaching the 100. So I breath deeply calming my nerves. I never was a scaredy-cat. Gosh...I hope it's gone, please let it be non-poisonous, without sharp teeth. 90.91.92.93...

Calming down I get back into my role as knight in silver armour. I will not let my king down. 98.99.100. "I am coming." I shout out loud, and open my eyes.

I'm all alone with the tree and his green personnel. For a moment, I forget the game and my role. I tiptoe across the soft mossy ground gently touching the ferns fine and slightly sticky texture. I feel like a fairy in a magic wood. Spinning on the tip of my toes, I elegantly dance through the ferns and around my tree. In my imagination I am light and elegant, with delicate see-through little wings on my back. Hopping from one leaf to the other, curling up in the ferns fingertips, my golden curls smoothly sliding into the open air, giving away my presence. There is a crackling noise from the king tree's crown, bringing me right back to reality. Little pieces of bark and some orangey-brown coloured leaves sail down my way and I think I see the tail of a squirrel vanish into the leaves.

Back in the now, I broaden my shoulders to cover the growing excitement in my tummy. I am a hunter, so I sink down to my knees, in a crouching position. I'm slowly moving through the woodland, my eyes dashing from one side to the other, catching every movement around me. All my senses are wide awake, recording every change. Some rustling in a nearby bush makes me freeze to ice. I turn and frantically search for my king. He is not too far from where I'm standing. I prepare to run, keeping the enemy bush in the corner of my eye. But nothing happens, so I move a few steps closer. The rustling dies down, nothing there. Annoyed about my unnecessary fear, I kick the bush with my short legs, causing myself more pain and most probably a new bruise. Less carefully I stroll further through our playground. Where are they? Why do I always need to count?

Lost in my anger, I don't at first notice that the tree in front of me has a yellow lining. The exact yellow of my youngest brothers jumper. "Rrrrrrraaaaahhhh…" Frederick William, or just Fred as we call him, jumps out of his hiding point and charges towards me with a roar. As quick as lightning, I turn on my heels and, with one big squeal, run back to my king. I can hear Fred close behind me. Sticks are cracking beneath our feet as we race through the ferns. A sudden bump and squeal behind me makes me realise that Fred must have tripped on one of the tree roots. But I can't take the risk of looking back. My brothers have cheated me this way too many times. I reach my king and gently clap on his bark. We are safe, safe for the moment, one more lumberjack to go. Behind me, Fred appears out of the green.

He is sobbing and his hair is a mess. His brown trousers have a large streak of green. He tries to hide his tears by wiping his face with his dirty hands, making him look like an Indian with face paint. With a sulk, he joins me at my saved king. He leans against the bark and slides down to his knees and starts brushing some of the loose remainders of leaves from his trousers. With a triumphant smile I dance around my own axis, pretending to flex my muscles. Fred just snorts. One more to go, just one more to go.

With newly found self-security, I move out of my comfort zone, knowing that Les will be a hard one to beat. Walking down close to the mossy path, I peer around every tree, always keeping an eye on my king and my first prisoner. Following the path, I soon come to a small brook that ambles through the forest to a pond. My father and Les went fishing there some time ago. The water is very cool and fresh. Most of it comes down from the hills. It's an ideal breeding point for sweet-water fish, and large schools gather in the pond. Dad and Les were very successful with their catch that day, and we had home-made fish and chips that night. The potatoes and peas were from our mother's garden. It was quite a feast, and I can still see Les sitting next to my Dad at the dinner table, his cheeks flushed with pride. Water has been his element ever since, which warns me to be careful. He must be close. I can almost smell him. I hop along the brook on my tiptoes. A wonderfully flat stone catches my eye. I pick it up and rub off the sand. It's coloured in a beautiful dark grey with a smooth surface. Its round and flat shape makes it an ideal skimming stone. I pop it into my skirt pocket for later – surely we will visit the pond.

Distracted by my find, I hadn't noticed two blue eyes peering down at me from the tree behind me. But the certainty of being watched reaches me within seconds. Turning round to face my feeling, I peer into Les's blue eyes. Eyes that I would later say could charm a duck from a pond! Les jumps from his hiding place with a bear's roar. The only thing I can do is run. Run for the life of my king.

Les is close behind me. I can feel him trying to grasp the ties of my apron to slow me down. Like a rabbit, I bounce from one spot to the other, making it hard for him to catch me. We are racing through the ferns and Fred is shouting and cheering. Buff ...

Les trips and spectacularly flies to the ground, making a loud bumping sound on landing. My king's legs have saved me once again. I run to my king and hug him with joy.

Les appears with messy hair and a little blood dropping from his bottom lip onto his brown shirt. His eyes are angry. How could he lose against his short-legged sister?

He nudges me hard, interrupting my victory celebration, and wipes his lips with the back of his hand. "Come on," he shouts. "Let's go to the pond."

The three of us move through the human-sized ferns down to the mossy path and follow the brook. Fred has found a long stick, and is drawing a line beside his footsteps while we move. I am holding my skimming stone in my skirt pocket, feeling the smooth surface. I can't wait to see it skip across the water. The pond lies in the middle of the forest. It's a peaceful opening with an old wooden bench at the one side, which invites you to just sit and watch the gently moving water. Reaching the bench, my brothers immediately start exploring the area in search of pebbles. I lay my pebble on the bench like a trophy. The bench is old and worn from the English weather. There is some writing on the backrest saying that the bench was donated by a Mrs Stevens. It is written that she loved to rest and watch the fish jump out of the water while trying to catch flies. There are many other carvings from lovers and spontaneous visitors. All the silly stuff people like to write.

I also search the surroundings, and find some more suitable pebbles. The three of us stand at the waterside and do our best to make our stones fly close to the surface. Every now and then, they touch the clear water and finally sink into the dark blue. This is definitely Les' game. His calm nature and strong arms are the ideal combination to make the stones skim far across the water. Mine are less successful. They bounce a couple of times, but then sink quickly. I decide to keep my trophy stone, and slip it back into the pocket of my skirt. Running out of skimming stones and slowly becoming bored, I wander through the woodland surrounding the pond.

I start collecting pretty flowers. Yellow and pink ones to make a necklace. Flowers have always captured my attention. Growing up on the countryside with two brothers shortly after the 1st World War has made me a tough cookie. But, nevertheless, pretty things like dainty flowers, my mother's pearls and cute clothes have always been my love. I like being a girl.

After I have collected a bunch, I sit down on the bench and carefully start looping one flower into the other.

My brothers are close. They are rolling up their trousers and kicking off their shoes. Les wants to try and catch a fish with his bare hands, like our grandfather showed us. Fred, a slightly less calm character, wants to try to catch one by taking a swing with his stick. They both slowly wade into the cool blue water. Fred is a little unsure once he feels the temperature of the water. But he will not let his brother down and stay on the bank with the girls ... well, with me.

They both get into position, calmly standing knee-deep, and carefully watching the water. Fred can't wait. He swings his bat and strikes the water surface, causing a big splash. Small waves chase each other across the pond, breaking the calm surface. Les is annoyed and waves Fred to move away from him, which isn't really understood.

Once the water have calmed down again, Les bends forward and dips his arms into the water and waits. It's peaceful in the forest. We can only hear some birds singing, calling each other. The trees' leaves rustle, sounding like they are chatting to each other. Swoosh...

Les' hands clap together, accidently washing his face with cool water. A big fish jumps out of the pond and right back in again. He has escaped his threatening doom, and is free to swim back to his school. Les swears some words that we're not supposed to know. His dark blond hair is wet and dripping down his forehead. He kicks the shiny blue water, splashing his giggling brother. Fred is so surprised that he steps back, slips and falls backwards into the pond. Quickly Les jumps towards him, grabbing him by the collar of his shirt and tears him out of the water.

Fred is spluttering all over the place and I'm standing straight upwards, shocked by the action. In our days, we didn't learn how to swim living in the countryside. Les drags

Fred out of the water and drops him on the soft waterside moss. Fred is soaking wet and still coughing up water. I sit down next to him and put my arm around him. Slowly the forest is darkening and we are late for dinner.

Once Fred has calmed down, we get back onto our feet and walk hand-in-hand up the path. Back the way we came, past the king-tree and out of the gate. We run down the steep hill with our arms stretched out, feeling like human airplanes. The air wizzes through our hair and we feel free. Free to go wherever the wind takes us. I feel like a wild bird travelling to faraway places. Never knowing what awaits me around the next corner. Wouldn't that be wonderful if we could just stretch our wings and fly?

I would be off to a mountain area with the greenest grass and most colourful wild flowers. What was I to know?

While walking down the lane to our house, we realise our state. Fred is soaked. I have muddy stains all over my apron and sleeves. Les has green stains all up his trousers and dried blood on his shirt. Mum will not be pleased. Looking at each other, we giggle and merrily run to our warmly lit home.

CHAPTER TWO

We live in a two-up one-down, small semi-detached and typically British village cottage. We spend most of our time on the ground floor. Our Mum, Edie, has arranged a warm kitchen/diner and living room. At the back of the kitchen, there is a small pantry and the back door leading out to our backyard, our bathroom facilities and the vegetable garden. In winter, I would hold back as long as possible before jumping into the bathroom shed. It was freezing in there. Not a place you would feel like taking your time in.

Upstairs, the three of us shared a cosy bedroom. My brothers sleep in a bunk bed, and I have a single mattress on the other side of the room. From our bedroom window we can see down onto the quite lane and up to our beloved hills of Strefford. For hours I would watch the sheep slowly moving from one green patch to the other. Up on the steep hills, they looked like little white snowflakes. I often imagined having an air-pencil in my hand, drawing the lines from one white dot to the other. Secret hillside drawings would appear for only me to see.

The second upstairs room is our parent's tiny bedroom. At night, it often happened that one of us would wake up due to a bad dream, a thunder storm or just because we were too excited to sleep. In these cases, we would tiptoe over the landing to our parent's bedroom and sneak into their warm bed.

So back to where we were. The three of us are standing in front of our warmly-lit house, giggling. Fred and I are kind of secretly jumping from one leg to the other. There will be a fight to get to the bathroom.

The curtains are not yet drawn, and it doesn't take long before Mum spots us through the window. She calmly walks over and opens the front door. Her expression is strict, and she scans us from top to bottom. "Looks like you all need a bath," she says without a smile in sight. "Come on, in with you and take your shoes off here. And yes, I mean exactly here!"

We watch her with big eyes, take off our shoes, and follow her into the house. "Mollie, you will be first in the tub. Les, help me fill the bath please. There's water boiling on the cooker."

In the kitchen, Mum has our large zinc bathtub ready for us. It is already half-filled with water. Les carries over a pot of boiling water and pours it into the waiting tub.

Mum helps me strip off my clothes and in I go. I can just sit with stretched-out legs and the warm water reaches my tummy button. It's great being the first. The water is still warm and clean.

With a big yellow sponge and soap. Mum washes me off and massages some shampoo into my blond wet curls. I enjoy this moment. "Dive down," she orders. My knees raise out of the water and down goes my head. I am under water and squeezing my eyes closed to avoid the shampoo making me cry. Mum combs my hair with her fingers to help ease out the shampoo. Getting short of breath and with cold knees, I decide it's time to come back to the surface. Mum is ready with a towel in her hand.

After drying me off, I slip into my pyjamas and quickly collect my little treasure out of my skirt pocket. My perfect skimming stone needs a safe home.

While my brothers are being bathed I run upstairs to our bedroom.

I have my very own treasure box under my bed. It's an old shoebox that I have decorated with pretty autumn leaves. I've cut my initials out of purple paper and stuck them in the middle of the box's lid. Inside, the box is lined with the original silky paper that the shoes were once wrapped in. Here, I keep all sorts of little things that I've found. I'm a natural born collector.

Carefully I lay my treasures out on my bed. I can remember the story behind every piece. With a proud smile on my face I stare down at my collection. Like in an official ceremony, I add my newly-found piece and give them time to introduce themselves.

Downstairs, I can hear that Fred is finished with his bath. I must hurry. My treasures are my secret belongings. I don't want by brothers to mix them all up, or to break or even take one of my dearest. Carefully, I place each piece back into my shoebox. Before adding my new skimming stone I decide to mark it with a big "M". From our shared desk I quickly take a pink felt-tip and draw a big "M" on the middle of it. That looks nice. The stone has a smooth surface and it feels cool and heavy in my hand. With my thumb, I stroke across the surface and close my eyes. It's as if I can feel how cool water from the brook washes over the stone, forming its shape, taking away the rough edges. Years and years must have passed until the stone found its perfect pebble shape. I am holding a witness of history, filled with stories of our secret wood, the brook and the fish that have found their way down through the wood to the pond. Their fins brush over the stone. Forgetting time I'm standing in our bedroom, my eyes closed with my stone in my hand. Sucking up stories of the past. Now they are here in my hand, in my bedroom, and will soon be in my treasure box.

Just as I am stashing my box back under my bed Fred enters the room. His hair is also wet from the wash and his cheeks have a warm glow. Luckily he's not too interested in what I am doing. He heads over to his satchel and fetches out a book. This reminds me that I should also be doing some homework. Fred loves school and learning. He is very eager. Numbers are his best friends. I like all the handicraft classes, but I am not too bothered with all the other subjects. But I enjoy spending time with my girlfriends on the schools playground.

"We have half an hour to get our homework done," Fred tells me. "At 6:30, Dad will be home and dinner ready."

Getting behind our books, we are soon joined by Les, who was the unlucky one to be bathed last.

Deep in our homework, we don't notice how time passes. We are brought back to reality as we hear the main door downstairs open and close. A warm gravy smell is filling our house. Les raises his head. "Dad's home," he shouts, slams his book closed and runs downstairs. Les loves Dad. He is a real Daddy's boy. Fred and I stash away our books in our satchels and also go downstairs.

Dad, Mum and Les are in the kitchen. Les is already eagerly telling Dad about our today's adventure. "I was in the pond, Dad. And a really big fish was resting above my hand. I could feel its texture. But it was too slippery. It got away. And then I saved Fred. He slipped and fell into the pond," he eagerly explains without a break. Dad is watching him with a proud smile on his face. "Never mind, Les. We can go this weekend and try again if the weather allows," Dad calms him down. "Oh yes, yes that would be great, Dad," Les excitedly responds.

From the corner of his eye, Dad spots Fred and me. His smile grows and he unexpectedly turns and charges towards us with a roar. We both start screaming and try to escape to the landing, but Dad has already caught us with his big strong arms. He swirls us around and squeezes us hard. "I got ya," he shouts. We giggle and pretend to fight against him. Dad, or Jack as he is called, is really funny and is always up to something.

Even though he spent over four years fighting for the country in the 1st World War, he never lost his warmth and good humour.

I never really understood the story about the Austrian duke called Franz Ferdinand and his wife, who were assassinated by an irredentist Serb. What did that have to do with

England? I don't even know where Austria or Serbia are, although they're obviously somewhere in Europe. And why did that lead to a world war? Why would the world want to split up families by taking fathers and older brothers to war because of a dead duke and his wife? Never knowing if they will ever come back home again. And if they do come home, how do they ever recover and become who they were again?

We were lucky. Our Dad came home as a respected captain. Mum always tells us he did really well, and that the men respected him and his orders. Thanks to his rank, we had a little extra money. That didn't make us rich or anything, but it enabled us to have warm dinners most days and clothes. Additionally my mother grew a lot of vegetables in our little patch of garden in the back. We always needed to eat all the vegetables up, because as she told us the vitamins will make us big and strong. I am not sure about the big. I was never going to be tall at the rate I was going.

"Dinner is ready," Mum calls. The five of us sit round our little dinner table. Tonight, we're having potatoes, some carrots and chicken with gravy. We are all really hungry after all the excitement in the wood. We dig in and enjoy the warmth growing inside of us. Mum watches us carefully, and now and then reminds us to calm down and only talk once we have swallowed.

Dad talks about his day at the dairy. He works in the Fulhampton dairy. It's not too far and he goes there on foot. He enjoys working with the farmers. Being in contact with locals is important for him. He loves to talk and be in good company.

After dinner, I help Mum in the kitchen while the boys and Dad sit around the fire. Dad tells them stories about his days in the trenches. Fred's eyes are at half-mast. He's soon peacefully sleeping on Dad's lap. Les is fully awake. His eyes are sparkling and his mouth is wide open. He is soaking up every word Dad says. It's as though he can see the story like a movie in front of his eyes.

Mum and I carefully stack the plates back in the dresser. "Thank you dear," my Mum says and gently strokes my hair. "It's time for bed children," Mum announces. "No, just a little longer," Les protests. Dad picks up the sleeping Fred. "Come on Les. Another fresh day awaits you tomorrow. You don't want to be too tired to enjoy it," says Dad. He carries Fred up the stairs, and Les follows pouting. I go up holding Mum's hand.

Once we are all tucked into bed, both our parents kiss our foreheads and off we go to the land of dreams.

In my dreams I am running down the hill, spreading my arms, ready to fly. Just like we did this afternoon. The grass under my bare feet is soft and damp from the night. Now and then, fine blades of grass get caught between my toes. I don't mind. I just wish they would be blades with dainty flowers on them. That would make my feet look magical, like some kind of fairy feet. The sun is rising and is warming my small body. Allowing me to widen and grow. I close my eyes and feel the warmth entering me. The wind is whistling through my blond curls. Freedom is all around me. I am at peace with the world. I feel carried, gently and safe. The soft grass is no longer beneath my feet. A blade of grass between

my toes loosens and drifts. My muscles are no longer clench-
ing. I am peacefully gliding.

Once these facts reach my brain, I carefully open my eyes.
I am no longer running down the hill. I am gently flying
through the air, carried by the wind. Looking down I can see
our home. Les and Fred have their heads stuck out of our
bedroom window and are frantically waving at me. I wave
back as if this would be the most normal thing in the world.
In my dream everything is possible. Everything is accepted.
Now I see Mum and Dad in the lane in front of our house.
They are also waving, and Mum is shouting something to
me. It is probably something like "Don't get dirty. Be home
on time for dinner. Don't talk to strangers." You know, the
things mothers always tell their children.

Carefully, I turn to one side and make a curve. I want to
sail over our magic wood and up the hills. The wind carries
me easily and I gently fly away from our house. Reaching
the wood, I gaze down at the trees crowns. There is one very
particularly large crown, and I know this is our king. There
is a bird's nest neatly built on one side of the king's crown.
There's a family of birds in the nest, a mother bird and three
baby birds. The baby birds are still naked, and are crouching
together to keep warm. The mother bird spots me, spreads
her wings and takes off. The three little birds chirp and clap
their wings, watching their mother leave their nest.

Soon she is up in the air next to me. Gliding by my side,
she joins my journey. She chirps some words to me and I
smile back. I obviously don't understand a word she says, but
I can feel the harmony between us. She is like a well-known
friend accompanying me. Together, we glide over the wood. I

believe I can hear the rushing of water along the brook below, making its way to the pond. Sailing above the trees, we reach the open space. Below, I can see the calm water surface of the pond. Every now and then a fat fish jumps out of the water for just a few seconds. Opening their mouths ready to catch insects and diving down into the fresh blue water. Otherwise there are no sounds, only the calm splashing of water every now and then. The old wooden bench is sitting next to the pond, waiting for visitors.

Flying further, we reach the end of the wood, and the rural hills take their place. A small stony path makes its way through the limited space the hills offer. Next to me, my mother bird friend chirps loudly, saying her goodbye. She curves and flies back to her territory, leaving me sailing by myself. I wave her goodbye and turn back to the hills. Getting a bit more daring, I decide to fly close to the side of the hills. The smell of damp soil and wet grass tickles my nose. I am picking up speed and the wind is cutting my cheeks. The temperature is dropping, and the wind is building up strength as I reach the summit.

I feel like I am on top of the world. No object blocks my view. I can see for miles. Our village is just little brown and grey spots scattered far below, with twisted lanes looking like snakes. Stretching myself, I'm standing in the air with my arms spread wide. My white nightie is blowing in the wind. I am strong and free. Everything lies beneath my feet, and makes me feel that all is possible. Feeling full of joy I somersault in the air. But doing it too many times makes me feel dizzy. Gentle arms are holding me, helping me keep my balance. I look around, and angels join me. They are in a kind of nightie dresses, like me. Their blond hair is flowing in the wind. They are beautiful. We smile at each other and dance in the air holding hands. I feel so happy, so beautiful and so safe.

In my sleep, I turn to my side and cuddle myself. With a happy smile on my face I am dreaming a beautiful peaceful dream. This night I will not wake and tiptoe over to my parent's bedroom. My dream is too wonderful.

CHAPTER THREE

The hands of time have turned forward somewhat.

My sheltered childhood is some years behind me. I am a 26-year-old single. Even though most of my girlfriends have settled down and married, I have not. It's kind of late for my age, I know, but I'm not too bothered about it. Even though I have turned into a pretty young lady, the time we are living in have made it hard to meet and court someone nice.

Once again the world is at war. A short man with small dark moustache in Germany is determined to take over the world. He wants to redesign it the way he feels it's most fit. As the leading country among the Allies, England is fighting for justice. Even though we are an island off the shore of Europe, we are being hit badly. Being out of the way in the countryside, we have a safer spot to live in. Nevertheless, daily goods are rare and hard to get. Our men have all gone off to war. In the newspapers, we read every day about the bombing in the cities. At night, we listen to the radio broadcasts and have a little suitcase ready with our most important belongings. Just in case the sirens go off during the night and we have to head for shelter at the nearby school. We pray before going to bed. We pray for the safety for our loved ones and against the growing fear in our heart. The untouchable feeling of freedom we experienced as children has gone. Reality has struck us hard.

I am still living with my parents in our two-up one-down small semi-attached village cottage. What was once the children's bedroom is now all mine. During my last years at school, I learned to sew and am quite talented. I make most of my clothes myself, and also do the odd frock for my mother or girlfriends.

Because of the war, I cannot fully devote myself to my needlework passion. As all the men are away at war, I have took on the milk round for the Fulhampton Dairy, where my father works. With a small open-back lorry, I drive up and down the small country lanes and make sure everybody gets their daily allowance of milk. I like my job and I enjoy meeting the neighbours and having a short chat.

In the area I have become know as "Mollie the Milk." A nickname I quite enjoy and which fills me with pride.

My brother Les joined the Air Force, and is courting Grace. She is a pretty young lady he knew from his school days. Once he is back from war, they want to marry and settle down. Les can't wait to have children of his own. He will be a great father one day.

Fred also joined the Air Force and is serving far away in South Africa. We don't hear too much of him due to the distance. Now and then we receive a letter and, if we are lucky, one or two exotic black and white pictures. He writes of the hot temperatures, the annoying flies and the dangerous backstreets of the city. But what impresses him most is the light. The light makes the sun feel much closer to the world. The power of Mother Earth feels reachable. The warm orange rays warm his heart. If only for a moment they can help him forget the fights and the poverty on the African streets.

He has met a lady called Joyce, who seems to make him happy and can help him forget about the war for some moments. I hope I will be able to meet her one day.

My milk round starts early in the morning. My father and I share our morning walk to the dairy. First, my Dad and I fill the wooden crates with bottles of milk. Once ready, we load the crates onto the back of the small lorry and off I go. By lunchtime I'm back at the dairy and unload the now empty crates. Sitting on the loading area of the lorry, I let my short legs dangle into the air. My father joins me and we enjoy our packed sandwich lunch. Sunlight is touching our faces and warming our cheeks. It's a lovely, late spring day. The sunlight lets us forget reality for a moment and takes us to a wonderful place.

The afternoons are all mine. I spend a lot of my time at home with my mother. In the warmer months, I love to help her in the garden. When it gets chillier, I spend more time indoors with the sewing machine, and design new skirts and dresses in flowery colours.

Today though, I'm going to treat myself to an afternoon tea with my girlfriends. We are meeting at a little tea shop close to the station. When the weather allows, we can sit outside and watch the trains and their passengers arriving and departing. We love watching people. Guessing where they are coming from or where their destiny lies. Who they are visiting and what they do. Today, we will surely be sitting outside, which makes the afternoon an even bigger treat.

Arriving at the coffee corner, I quickly spot my girl-friends. Jane is sitting, gently pushing the pram of her newly-born back and forwards. She gave birth to a pretty little boy a month ago. She is living with her mother just a few minutes away from my home. Once Tom, her husband, is back from the war, they want to try to get a mortgage from the bank to buy a little house of their own. Jane and Tom got married shortly before the war started. Tom has been back for short breaks in-between, but he hasn't seen his little boy yet. I think he is somewhere in France, and should be back for his next leave soon. We are keeping our fingers crossed that this day will come. But we never speak it out loud.

Jessie is sitting on the other side of the table. Her young-est is already walking and making her bounce out of her chair every now and then to fetch him back. Number two, a sweet little girl, is sleeping in her pram. Jessie married early, and lives in a one-up one-down little terraced house close to her parents.

"Mollie the Milk, here we are!" Shouts Jessie across the table. We beam at each other and I take my place. My seat is a very good one. I have full view to the nearby station, which puts me into the pole position for watching. We order our tea and start chatting about all the village gossip. These are rare moments I truly enjoy.

A large black train arrives at the station making a lot of noise. The doors open and people start pouring out. There are several soldiers leaving the train, dressed in smart uniforms and carrying large backpacks. Family members are waiting for them on the platform, and a lot of hugging and drying of tears is going on. The train seems to have emptied. An elderly lady dressed in a pale green dress and washed-out flowery apron catches my eye. Her grey hair is neatly combed into a bun. Her head is turning from one carriage to the other, searching for a loved one. Suddenly her hands clap to her cheeks and she runs towards one of the carriages. A tall man in a brown uniform is climbing down the steep steps of the carriage. In one hand a leather carrier bag, the other hand holding his uniform hat. His hair is dark and neatly combed to one side. His appearance is elegant, but I feel a cloud of pain surrounding him, clinging to his body, not letting him go. Too much has been seen, too much has happened. Will he ever find peace?

Once he is safely down on the platform, he drops his bag and opens his arms to hug the elderly lady, who presses her cheek to his chest. He fondly kisses her hair and holds her in his arms. Time stands still. All the bad things of the world seem to fade away. The evil ghosts are evaporating and a wave of warmth takes its place. Peace has returned home.

His size, his uniform and his nature causes a prickling feeling to grow deep down in my tummy. I am feeling warm and safe by just watching them. After a few seconds, he elegantly puts his hat on and picks up his leather bag. He lays his arm around the shoulders of the lady, and they slowly walk away from the station.

Jane has noticed me watching the touching scene. "That's Jack Meredith and his mother Julie," she says. "His father John sadly died a few months ago. He is single," she adds with a wink. I scold her with a look. "Well, it's time that Mollie the Milk finds her cream," Jessie squeezes out between laughter.

We all giggle, and I shyly turn my head to see the couple vanish behind a building. The warm sparkling feeling in my tummy stays, and makes me curious.

We finish our tea, and Jane and I walk up the main street towards our homes. Jane is watching me from the corner of her eye while pushing her new-born. "You know that we could organize a drink at the pub with Jack. He is a little older, but did you see him in his uniform? I would say he's quite a chap."

I'm too shy to look at her. Instead, I study the pavement beneath my feet. "I don't know. I'm sure he just wants to spend some time with his Mum. It must be a hard time for her, losing her husband and her son being away at the war. If it's meant to be, we will meet," I add.

"Well, you know Mollie, sometimes you need to do something for your luck. You're a beautiful young lady. I anyway don't understand how you have managed to stay unmarried. But suit yourself." We carry on walking in silence until we reach our homes.

At home, I help Mum in the kitchen. We prepare a warm dinner for the three of us. Later on, we listen to the radio, hoping to hear no bad news of our troops abroad. The fear of losing one of our loved ones is growing every day. We pray for their safe return home.

Turning in my single bed, I dream of the mysterious man I saw today at the train station.

In my dream, I'm standing at the station in a newly sewn dress. It is a beautiful dark purple. An elegant cut that makes me look much taller then I actually am. An elegant patent purse is dangling over my arm, perfectly matching my shoes. My blond curls are loosely tied at the back of my head. Over my shoulders, a fine silk scarf is protecting my arms from the cool spring breeze.

I'm waiting for the black train to arrive. In the distance, I can hear the hissing of the engine, and I know my love is close. Brakes are squealing and there's smoke in the air. Around me, the questioning sound of people waiting has risen. I stay calm on the platform. I know my love has arrived. The train doors open and people pour out onto the platform. Excitement grows around me. Some people are pushing and shoving, trying to be in the front row. Names are cried out. I calmly wait.

Couples are finding each other. Love and joy is in the air. People are chatting, tears are dropping. And I'm still standing at the platform, not moving a spot.

My surroundings have calmed down, and many reunited couples are joyfully leaving the scene. My focus is fixed on the carriage of the train in front of me. My love has arrived.

A cloud of smoke slowly drifts past the train. As the air clears, I see a tall man standing on the top step of the carriage in front of me. He is elegantly dressed in a brown uniform. His hair is neatly combed to one side, his hat is tucked under is arm and, in the other, he's holding his shiny leather bag. His big brown eyes scan the platform, come to a halt and rest on me. Slowly, he takes one step after the other until he reaches the platform. His shiny leather bag drops to the ground.

He stands and looks me into the eye without any movement of the muscles in his face. We stand and look at each other. Time stands still. Looking in his eyes, I can see deep into his soul. His fear and his hopes open up to me. I can see the pain, the pain of weeks, months of being on the battlefield. Seeing the fear and helplessness of so many. Watching his fellows fall. Innocent children and women cry. How much can a man take?

A tear slowly makes its way down my pale cheek. But I don't move, I'm captured in his gaze.

He opens his arms to greet me. My legs go into motion and I am lying in his arms. Pressing myself towards him, resting my cheek on his strong chest. His arms close around me. I feel safe, I feel at home. Nothing can harm me in this precious moment.

His hand lifts my chin and he looks into my watery eyes. He smiles at me, lowers his head and our lips meet. He feels warm and strong. He is home.

No sirens howl that night. I'm safe in my single bed. My dream has taken me far away and into the arms of love. I rest peacefully.

My alarm wakes me early the next morning. It's time to become "Mollie the Milk." Sitting on the side of my bed, I rub my eyes, and my mind goes back to my dream. I blush and shyly stare down at my feet.

I can hear my father making his way down the stairs on the other side of the house. Quickly, I wash my face with some icy cold water from my washing bowl. Slip on a flowery dress and comb my curls to a loose bun at the back of my head.

Downstairs, Dad is having a cup of tea. A second cup is sitting ready for me on the kitchen table. "Morning love," Dad says. I smile at him and quickly drink my black tea. The warm fluid immediately awakens my bones and warms my body.

We make our way to the dairy together. It's chilly out, and the lane is still dark. Only one or two houses have already lit their lights. It's a peaceful morning.

It's the normal procedure at the dairy. First we fill the bottles of milk, and then we load the crates onto the open back of the lorry. The sun is just starting to rise as off I go.

My milk round is not much different from all the other days. I meet many neighbours, have a quick chat and carry on to the next house.

Only three more homes left to deliver to. I drive up a little lane to an old cottage. There is an apple orchard at the back of the house. The apple trees are in bloom and look like they are covered with fresh snow. I sit and gaze at the beauty of nature for a moment.

The front door of the house opens and an elderly lady walks out. Her hair is grey and combed to a bun. She is wearing a pale blue dress and a flowery, washed-out apron.

I immediately recognize her. She is John Meredith's mother. The couple I watched at the train station yesterday. I blush thinking of my dream last night, and my cheeks turn pink.

I have been to this house several times, but I never met anyone. The small milk carton with a note asking for only one bottle of milk every second day was the only evidence of habitation I had ever seen.

Mrs Meredith is standing waiting for me, so I quickly jump out of the lorry. She looks at me with a smile on her face. "Mollie the Milk, right?" she asks. I nod. "My son has come home at last. He is on a one-week leave. For the next week I therefore need a bottle of milk a day, if that's possible," she politely asks. "Oh that is good news! I am so happy for you. Certainly, one bottle a day, that'll be fine," I confirm. She smiles at me, and I fetch her one bottle of milk from the back of the lorry.

When I get back to hand over the milk, I'm surprised to see John. He has joined his mother waiting for me. I feel my cheeks turn bright pink again and my knees wobble. Can he tell?

Jack has placed his arm around his mother, and they are both are smiling at me. I hand Mrs Meredith her bottle of milk. Jack is watching me. "Thank you," he says. "Is it true that the village calls you "Mollie the Milk?" he adds. I smile shyly and nod. "Well, thank you for making sure my mother gets her ration. We are having a drink with some of the locals down at the Craven Arms tonight. Would you like to join us?" he asks. I'm quite surprised. Nowadays, money is too tight to offer drinks. And why would they invite their milk lady?

Jack is still watching me with bright eyes. I smile at him and accept his invitation, and quickly jump back into the lorry. I am beaming all across my face. Jack Meredith has invited me. I'm so excited. Setting the small lorry into motion. I carefully turn and drive down the little lane. In the back mirror I can see them both waving as they turn together and go back to their house.

There are two more homes on my list.

When I arrive home after my packed lunch break. I'm still quite excited. My Mum is in the garden. I quickly change into my garden gear and join her. She is sowing vegetables and I help her dig small holes for the seeds. I am still beaming all over my face, which my mother doesn't miss.

"Everything all right, Mollie?" she asks. "Jack Meredith is back from war for a one-week leave. I saw him and his mother today on my milk round," I tell her. "They have invited me for a welcome-home drink at the Craven Arms tonight."

My mother is examining my face carefully. "Well that is unusual. Looks like you are quite excited to go. I didn't know you knew them?" "Well, I don't really Mum. I was quite surprised to be invited. I think he just wants to thank me for delivering the milk to his mother while he's been away. I heard that his father passed away not too long ago. It must be hard for Mrs Meredith all alone." My mother drops another seed into the ready-made tiny hole. "Yes it must be," she adds not taking her eyes off me while patting the earth back. "Well I hope you enjoy yourself," she smiles. I smile back, and we carry on with the gardening.

CHAPTER FOUR

Its 5 p.m., and I am in my bedroom washing the dust from my face. I comb my curls and decide to only pin the sides back with a small clip. There is a knock at my door and my mother pokes her head into my room. "I have some eyeliner and blush for special occasions," she says, beaming at me. "Do you want to have some?" She offers. "Will you help me?" I ask her.

I've never used make-up before. It's not something you can get in these times. Smiling at me, she pushes herself to me onto the little chair in front of my desk. "You are a very pretty young lady, Mollie. A little blush will make you look fresh. I don't think you'll need the eyeliner." With a soft brush, she carefully applies some pink coloured powder to my cheeks. "There you go! Makes you look like you've had a little sun. It looks healthy and fresh," she smiles.

"You'd better get dressed or you will be late." She stands up, kisses my forehead and leaves my room.

I pick a pretty, light-pink-coloured dress with little flowers around the neck that I made some weeks ago. At last I have an opportunity to wear it.

I slip on my Sunday shoes, take my purse and go downstairs.

Dad is home, and he and Mum are standing on the landing proudly looking at me. Gosh, I'm only invited to a welcome-home drink. They seem to be getting their hopes a little high. I feel like a princess going to her graduating ball.

They both kiss me goodbye, and I walk down the quiet lane. The Craven Arms is not too far from where we live. Arriving at the small pub, I start to feel a bit nervous. I'm probably also getting my hopes a little high. They were certainly only being nice to me.

A couple brushes past me and vanish into the pub. It's getting chilly outside, and I feel a little silly standing in front of the door. Through the windows, I can see some people happily chatting away. Through the other window, I can see a tall man standing there. He turns and gazes out of the window. It's him. He spots me outside, and his gaze captures mine. Our eyes are locked for what feels like minutes, but are only a few seconds. He smiles a bright smile, turns and walks to the pub door.

My heart is beating and I feel my palms go damp. I am definitely nervous.

"Mollie, you came," he smiles as he appears through the door. He stretches out his arm and takes my hand. "You're so pretty, you look wonderful. I am so happy you're here. Now, come on in with you! It's chilly out here." I'm holding his hand and following him into the cosy little pub. Hopefully the dimmed evening light covers my blushing, I think to myself.

The fireplace is lit and is heating up the small room. There are maybe 10 people sitting at low tables, happily chatting with each other. The owner of the pub is standing behind the bar with a grim expression on his face.

"Let me take your jacket," Jack offers. He takes my jacket and hangs it on a hook close to the entrance. "What would you like to drink?" he asks me, leading me to the bar. He is still holding my hand. "I will have some tonic if that's okay," I ask. "With some gin, I hope?" he smiles. I have only once ever had a little gin. It made me dizzy and warm at the same time. I nod, not wanting to be rude.

Jack orders my drink from the grim looking owner behind the bar. Jack is drinking a dark beer. We clink our glasses and I take a sip of my gin and tonic. It's cool, a little sparkly and has a bitter but refreshing after taste. It's nice.

Taking my glass in one hand and leading me with the other, Jack guides me to a little table close to the window. We sit together and he tells me stories about his travels abroad. He has been to many countries in Europe. But not in way you'd like to visit a place.

He tells me about France and Belgium where he has spent most of his time. They eat frog legs and snails in France - I can hardly imagine it. He has tried them both on occasions, but luckily hasn't taken a liking to either of them. English homemade food is what he misses, and his mother of course. He wasn't able to be with her when his Dad sadly passed away this winter. He was stuck in a small French village, and only got the news two weeks after his death. This spring was the first opportunity he has had to travel home.

He tells me a lot about the people and the KSLI troops he is serving for. KSLI stands for the King's Shropshire Light Infantry. Light Infantry means that they don't have many mechanised vehicles. They are on foot most of the time, with only their rifles. For longer distances, they are loaded onto the back of large lorries, squashed together like sardines. But they mostly spend a lot of time at the same spot. Protecting small villages from being recaptured by the enemy.

So far they have been lucky and haven't lost many men. His eyes darken, and a sad crease forms between his brows. He looks down at the table and follows the pattern of the wood with his forefinger.

Instinctively I can feel his pain of loss. We sit together without speaking. It's not an uncomfortable feeling though. Our thoughts just need time to settle.

My gin is warming my tummy and loosening my muscles. I am feeling warm and cosy in the little pub. Behind the bar, I can see the fingers of the clock ticking much too fast. I have to be up early tomorrow morning for my milk round. Jack seems to realize my uneasiness. "Would you like me to walk you home?" he offers. I blush. "No, you should stay here with your friends. I'll be fine," I assure him. "Well Mollie, I was taught by my mother to never let a lovely lady walk home alone at night. It would be my pleasure. Let me fetch your coat." Jack jumps to his feet before I can protest. He is back in a second with my coat in his hand. He holds it open for me so I can easily slip my arms in.

Holding the door open for me, he leads me out of the pub. We silently walk up the lane together. We are soon in front of my home. Jack turns and takes my hand. "It was a pleasure to meet you Mollie. I would very much like to see you again soon." Once again I blush, and stare down to my shoes. "Well, I'll be on my milk round tomorrow. I'm sure I will see you then, right?" I reply. "I won't be home, unfortunately. I have promised my Mum to take care of some errands," Jack replies. "How about this weekend? Are you free on Saturday? The weather should be nice. How about a picnic in the park?"

I can't hide my excitement. It's all over my face. "I would love to. Thank you!" "My pleasure," Jack returns. "I will pick you up here at 2 p.m." With a face glowing full of pride, I unlock our front door and wave Jack goodbye. I am overwhelmed. Nobody has ever asked me to a picnic.

The following two days don't seem to pass quickly enough. I do my milk round as usual. As Mrs Meredith has increased her milk order, I'm now visiting their house daily. As much as I hoped to see Jack, I was unfortunately disappointed. He wasn't home.

I awake early on Saturday morning. I'm too excited to sleep. Downstairs, Mum has prepared a bath for me. Our tub is standing in the middle of the kitchen floor.

Sitting in the warm water with the first rays of sunlight tickling my back through the window, I relax and enjoy the feeling. Dad is out, so I have time and can enjoy the ritual. Mum helps me with my hair. She gently massages some shampoo into my curls. Her strong fingers loosen all the tension and my mind relaxes. I dive down to wash off the shampoo. Warm water rushes over my face and my ears pop. What a wonderful way to start a perfect Saturday.

After I have dried off, I carefully comb my hair into shape. Scanning through my wardrobe, I chose a pale yellow frock and a cream-white long sleeved blouse that my mother gave me for my birthday last year.

Looking into the mirror, I decide to tie a yellow ribbon in my hair. This makes me look young and carefree.

Downstairs, Mum has prepared some breakfast for us. We enjoy our cup of tea and some toast with marmalade in silence. We let the radio play in the background. Just in case there's any news from the front. We haven't heard much lately. I'm not sure if I should regard this fact as good, or just the quiet before the storm.

"I will be off to the market soon," Mum tells me. "What time will Jack pick you up?" she asks. "He'll be here at 2 p.m.," I beam. "Oh, that's good! That will give you some time for yourself. "Mollie, dear, you look beautiful and very happy," she sincerely smiles.

Mum has left the house. It's peaceful and the sun is shining through the kitchen window. I decide to take a book and sit in the backyard.

We have an old wicker chair leaning against the house. I plunge down into the chair and lean my head against the old wood. From here, I have full view of our little vegetable patch. I just sit and watch. It's as if I can see the runner beans arms sneaking up the wooden poles. Their young leaves are a lovely fresh green.

The whole garden will soon be in full bloom. This is my favourite time of the year. Pretty flowers have always been a passion of mine. My mother is very proud of her vegetables. They are delicious, and pep up every meal.

I curl my legs up onto the chair and just sit and gaze. The sunlight is blinding my sight. Closing my eyes, I enjoy the warmth. I am feeling like a butterfly in its cocoon, dangling from the branch of a tree. Soon my time will come, and I will spread my colourful wings and fly. I would fly from one pretty flower to the other.

Slowly I doze off in the backyard. Falling into a flowery butterfly dream. Time has no space. It's only about the now. My pretty wings are flapping and I am sailing across a meadow. A beautiful big yellow flower catches my eye, and I decide to land and take a rest. Sitting in the middle of the flowers bud, I look forward across the meadow. The field is a canvas of bright colours. It's a beautiful sight.

A knock at the door wakes me. What's the time? Oh my, how long have I dozed off for?

Jumping to my feet, I walk back into the living room. Through the window, I can see Jack with a basket. My heart misses a beat and I gaze at him for a moment. He is dressed in brown trousers and is wearing a crisp white shirt. His dark hair is carefully combed to one side, making him look very elegant.

Before opening the front door, I quickly glance in the mirror. I look lovely and fresh, and the yellow ribbon in my hair gives me a playful finish. The sun has produced a fine pink colour on my cheeks.

Opening the front door is opening a new chapter in my life.

We spend a lovely afternoon in the park. Jack has thought of everything, and he has brought a red tartan blanket for us to sit on. The fabric is soft and we kick off our shoes, lean against a tree and stretch out our legs on the blanket. From here, we have a wonderful view across the park, and the trees branches protect us from too much sunlight.

Jack has packed some crackers and cheese. It's a delicious treat. Cheese is quite rare these days. To top off our afternoon snack, he has carefully wrapped two teacups in newspaper. His thermos flask has kept the Early Grey warm. Sitting in the park with china teacups filled with warm black tea, crackers and cheese makes me feel like a princess. It couldn't be more perfect.

We talk about our lives, our wishes and dreams. I love to hear him talk about his future life. He cannot wait for the war to be over. He wants to come home for good, help his mother in the orchard and hopefully one day see his own children play between the trees. The country is where he wants to be.

It's as though I can see the picture in front of me. Jack and I standing hand in hand next to our house. The apple trees are blooming and we can hear giggling behind the trees. Our little boy and girl are chasing each other, playing hide and seek between the trees. Jack decides to sneak up and surprise our little boy, who is nagging his sister by pulling her skirt.

Quietly, he creeps behind the tree and surprises our son with a big roar. He picks him up over his shoulder and gently spanks his bottom. A lot of squealing and laughter is going on. I smile and run over to join them.

Jack pokes me back to earth. Oops, I was dreaming. My cheeks colour bright pink, and I shyly stare down onto the tartan blanket.

After finishing our tea and crackers we lie down on the blanket and stare into the crown of the tree. Small white clouds are passing by and we play cloud shape guessing.

Jack gently takes my hand into his. My pulse starts racing, and I don't know what to do or say. He turns onto his side and watches me. "I will have to go back to Belgium in two days," he tells me. "I would like to keep in touch with you. I have enjoyed every moment with you very much." His warm smile makes butterflies flap their wings deep down inside of me. He raises my hand to his lips and tenderly places a kiss on the back of my hand. For a few seconds the world around me vanishes. My butterflies are going crazy and my heart is pounding. "I would very much like …" I manage to stammer. We smile at each other, and Jack squeezes my hand.

Two days later I'm standing on the station platform waiting for Jack and his mother, Mrs Meredith. The past days have flown. It's as if they were just a beautiful dream. For the first time in my life I'm in love. In love with a tall handsome man. A man who is going back to war. Nervously, I play with my fingers. Jack and Mrs Meredith arrive. Jack is dressed in his brown uniform and looks very smart. Mrs Meredith has a tissue in her hand. Her eyes are watery and her face gives away her fears.

The three of us stand in silence on the platform and wait for the train. In the distance, I can hear the train's engine chattering. Soon we can see smoke and hear the squealing of the breaks. Jack turns to his mother and presses her to his chest. She cannot hold back her tears any longer. Quietly she weeps and tries to dab her tears with her tissue. He kisses her cheeks and smiles at her. "Hopefully I will be back for Christmas, Mum. Don't worry! God is with me."

Then he turns to me. Instinctively we hug each other and I too press my cheek to his chest. After a moment he releases me and his dark eyes pin mine. Carefully, he lifts my chin and gently presses his warm lips on mine. I am captured. I cannot move. My heart feels like it's beating right up into my head and my butterflies are dancing deep within me. Around me the world has vanished. It's only him and me.

His lips slowly leave mine and he strokes a loose lock of hair behind my ear. "I am very much looking forward to reading your letters, my beautiful Mollie," he says smiling a warm smile at me. I smile back. Mixed feelings of joy and pain confuse me.

Jack picks up his leather bag. Turns and jumps up the steep steps to the carriage. Before the doors close, he turns, smiles and waves to us.

The train goes back into motion. The wheels are squealing, and smoke fills the air.

The two of us are left alone on the platform, watching the big black train leave the station.

CHAPTER FIVE

My newly found love has left, and I'm back in my daily routine. Our short memories together are now my most valuable treasures. But I will not keep these in my decorated shoebox under my bed. They are deep inside me.

Every other day, I sit down and write a letter to Jack. I tell him of my daily adventures on my milk round. About what is going on in the village and how the seasons are changing.

But I also write about how I dream about him coming home. How I will be standing on the platform waiting for him. How we will fall into each other's arms when he arrives.

Everything happened very quickly, I know. But that's how it is when your country is at war. You don't know how much time you have. So you enjoy every moment as if it could be the last.

Being in weekly contact through our letters gives us the time to get to know each other. I gorge on every word he writes to me. Every night before I go to bed, I re-read his letters and swallow down every word. I dream of his dreams, and he does the same.

One late autumn day, I'm just coming back from my usual milk round. A letter from Jack is waiting for me at home on the kitchen counter. I carefully open the envelope - I don't want to accidentally rip the paper.

Sitting down next to the fireplace, I open the two crisp white pages.

Jack writes about his days in Belgium. He has had a rough week. The Nazis have attacked their village, and they lost some territory. They have been fighting back ever since, and have been able to drive the enemy back out of the village. But this fight has cost a lot of lives.

The situation has settled and the Allies have made good progress pushing the Nazis back behind their line. They believe the war could soon be over.

Jack has requested a leave at the end of the year, and, if the situation stays stable, his chances are looking good. It would be his first Christmas at home since the start of the war.

My breath stops. Jack is coming home. I just know it. Christmas with Jack!

Staring out of the window, I imagine seeing snowflakes fall. Children are joyfully playing outside. They are building snowmen and singing Christmas carols. My parents, Jack and myself are preparing our Christmas lunch. We are wearing woolly jumpers and beaming at each other while peeling the potatoes. A turkey roast is in the oven. It's our first feast together.

"Mollie, everything okay?" My mother calls through the back door. "Yes, definitely. Jack will be back for Christmas!" I shout.

"Well, that is news!" She says entering the room. She is smiling too. We didn't only get a letter from Jack, but also from Les. Les is planning to be back for Christmas too. Our family will almost be reunited.

Only Fred will be missing. Due to the distance, we don't have any high hopes that they will send him back home for a well-deserved break. But he is still seeing Joyce, and things are going well. We are sure he will be able to find a touch of home in South Africa if he can spend Christmas Day with her family.

I take Jack's letter and dance up the stairs to my bedroom. I want to write back to him immediately.

The weeks till Christmas just don't want to pass. The temperatures are falling and our magical wood has turned a golden colour. I love to watch the trees move in the wind from the window of my bedroom. Like a chorus of tall men and women dressed in golden gowns. They are slowly swaying in unison from one side to the other. Not missing a beat.

In my thoughts, I try to send the picture to my brothers. I know they would love the sight.

In my free time I go for walks through the forest, and collect pretty, coloured leaves to decorate our home. The autumn colours amaze me over and over again. Our nature is beautiful. My time in the wood and up the valley takes me back to our childhood. For some moments, I can forget my worries. My worries for my brothers far away, and of course for Jack.

The temperature has fallen further and the trees have lost their golden gowns. Winter has arrived. Wisely, I decide to wear my warm jacket. At first I was trying to avoid it, as it doesn't let me show off my newly made dress. My mother and the dark clouds in the sky won the argument though. So I am standing at the station platform in my thick brown jacket. Wishing I could afford one of the more colourful, slim looking versions I have seen some women wear in pictures. The wind is howling down the narrow platform and my curls are blowing across my face. I adjust my hat, hoping the cold air won't carry it away. The last thing I want is to have to chase it across the platform. It would probably end up in a wet puddle. How would that make me look?

I'm nervously fidgeting with my jacket, trying to make it look straight. My mother has lent me her brooch. It's of two owls sitting on a little branch. The owls' feathers are gold plated. They have large green eyes and ivory coloured breast feathers. The piece matches my jacket quite well and I hope it peps up my appearance. I want Jack to feel proud when he sees me.

Mrs Meredith has decided to wait at home for her son. The cold weather has got to her bones, and she is not too good on foot lately. So I am standing by myself waiting for my love to come home.

The station clock strikes 12:30. The train should already be here. Trust the English railway to make a lady stand in the cold! I frown at the thought, and look along the tracks. Some more people have gathered on the platform. Suitcases are standing ready to be loaded into the carriages. A mother with her two children is shivering close to me. A whistle in the distance interrupts the chattering of her teeth. This must be the train arriving. Excitement rises deep inside me. I no longer feel the cold.

In the distance, I can see grey smoke rising into the sky, soon followed by a big black train.

Brakes are squealing and the platform has suddenly come alive. People are gathering, picking up their suitcases and saying their last goodbye to loved ones.

The train halts and the carriage doors spring open. Travellers are pouring out onto the platform. My eyes dash from one carriage door to the other. And there he is! Dressed in his smart brown uniform. His leather bag in one hand and a red rose in the other. Seeing him takes my breath away. Clouds of smoke sway past the train, robbing my sight of him for a moment. The smoke rises, and I can't see him on the top of the carriage steps anymore. For a moment I feel confused, like waking up from a lovely dream much too soon. Then he's there, one foot away from me. His dark eyes are watching me intensely, glowing with love. His leather bag drops to the ground and his arm reaches for me. My heart is pounding. My feet seem glued to the cold, grey platform. I'm not able to move an inch. The next thing I know, I'm pulled into his strong arms. He feels warm. The fabric of his uniform is stiff and has a rough touch. It smells of gunpowder, smoke and metal. A shiver runs through me and I feel him tighten his embrace.

Around us, the platform is bustling, but we don't notice. We just stand and hold each other. The carriage doors close and the train's whistle wakens us. Jack loosens his grip and looks down at me. Gently, he strokes my cheeks and tugs a loose strand of hair behind my ear. Shyly, I look up at him through my lashes. He looks tired and his skin is dry from the wind. It's a strange feeling being so close to him after so many months apart. Not that I wouldn't want to be so close. It just takes time to get used to. My butterflies are flapping their wings like mad in my tummy. He tilts my head back and our lips meet. The world around me swirls and vanishes. It's only him and me.

The next two days till Christmas are all about preparing our feast and spending time with Jack. The day of his arrival, I had afternoon tea at his mother's house. The next day, we spent the afternoon together wandering through our little village. Jack is very tired. He needs a lot of rest. The past weeks of battle have taken their toll. He and his comrades spent days and nights protecting their little village in Belgium from the Germans. Again and again they were under attack. Many of his comrades will never come home. I thank God for sending him safely home to us.

My parents have invited Jack and his mother to our Christmas roast. Les, who came home a few days ago, is spending Christmas with Grace and her parents. They got engaged the day he arrived back. He surprised her by going down on his knee as soon as he arrived at the station. It was quite a commotion. Grace was in tears, my mother was in tears and I believe some other passer-bys too. They are planning to get married next spring. As soon as Les gets some more leave.

On the 25th of December, Mum and I are up early preparing the house and our Christmas lunch. It has been some time since we have had visitors, and Mum is quite nervous. She has been cleaning the house for days, making everything look spick and span. Dad has been able to buy a small turkey from one of the farmers who deliver milk to our dairy. The plucked bird has been in our oven since yesterday afternoon. The delicious smell of white meat made our mouths water all night. The roast is now waiting on our kitchen counter for its final touch. By one o'clock everything is ready, and the bird is back in the oven. Jack, Mrs Meredith and my Dad are happily chatting near the fire. Mum and I fill our best china with the steaming vegetables. "Dear, the turkey is ready. Can you please carry it over to the table and make sure everybody gets a nice piece?" Mum asks Dad with a proud smile.

Minutes later, we are all merrily sitting around the table digging into our meal. Mum's vegetables are delicious and the turkey is an extraordinary treat. I don't think there will be many leftovers today.

After our meal, I help Mum in the kitchen. Mrs Meredith is having a rest in one of our armchairs next to the fireplace. Dad and Jack are in the backyard enjoying some Belgium cigarettes Jack has brought back with him. My Dad is leaning against the wall. His knee is bent so that the sole of his shoe is resting against the wall. Jack is standing in front of him, and they seem to be in a serious discussion. I wonder what they are talking about. "Don't worry my love, it'll be men's talk. You know, talk about the war, that kind of think," my Mum assures me while washing the last dishes. Absently I nod, and dry the next plate. Outside, I can see my Dad lean forward and pat Jack on the shoulder. Whatever they are talking about, they seem to understand each other.

Later on this day, the five of us sit together around the fireplace. Mrs Meredith and Dad soon nod off to sleep. Mum just cannot sit still. She wants everything to be perfect, and is constantly jumping to her feet.

"Mollie, how about going for a walk? Some fresh air and movement will do us good!" Jack asks me. "Sure. That's a nice idea. A walk will do me good after all I've eaten," I smile at him.

Dressed in our warm coats, we walk up the lane, and soon reach the cattle grid. Jack helps me across and we slowly make our way up the steep hill. The fresh cold air is cutting our skin, and I'm glad I have my gloves with me. Arriving at the entrance to the wood, we decide to take a rest on the top step. We are both slightly panting from walking up the hill, and it looks like we are both blowing smoke into the icy air. Our large lunch and the glass of wine have tired our legs.

From this point, we have a lovely view down onto the village. We can see countless rooftops and smoking chimneys. Luscious green meadows meet in the distance, only separated by low stony walls or dark green hedges. Making them look like some kind of board game. All is quiet. The village seems to be at rest.

We huddle together to keep warm, and Jack puts his arm around me. "You can't imagine, Mollie, how good it is to be home," Jack says, gazing into the distance. "Everything is so innocent here. It's like being in a bubble. Far away from all the world's problems. Your letters helped me to survive the days in the dark - I read them every night. They gave me hope and made me believe in the future," Jack carries on, turning to me. "Mollie, I want to share my future with you." He gently strokes my cheek with his hand. I blush and nervously start playing with my fingers. "I did the same. I read your letters every night. Every day I hoped to find a new envelope from you on our kitchen counter," I manage to reply. I feel tears building in the corner of my eyes. Tears of fear that I felt over the last months. Tears of hope and tears of happiness and gratitude. Jack carefully dries a single drop that escapes and runs down my face with his thumb. Kneeling in front of me, he takes my hands into his. "Mollie Price, you have been the light helping me find home. The words in the letters you sent me are my comfort in the cold nights. My dream is to spend my future with you. Please marry me!"

I am gob-smacked. With an open mouth I stare at him, trying to follow what he has just asked me. Has he asked me to marry him? Yes, he has! I'm getting married! Mary Eileen getting married? Jack is watching me, trying to read my reaction. "Well?" he smiles. "You're not going to leave me here kneeling like this? Are you?" I manage to recover control over my jaw. "Yes, yes, I will marry you!" I reply with a joyful smile, jump to my feet and throw my arms around his neck, nearly knocking him over. Jack's strong arms catch me and we lay in each other's embrace. Feeling our warmth, feeling our hearts beat. Kissing each other, we forget about the view and the cutting cold air. We are in our own little cocoon.

CHAPTER SIX

Christmas has passed and I have started the New Year as the fiancé of Jack Meredith. I love the sound of the words. I cannot stop telling everybody. Mollie the Milk has found her cream! How about that!

Jack has gone back to the front. We are confident that our marriage plans will bring him a leave late this spring. While I'm still waiting for good news, Les' plans have progressed. He will be back home to marry Grace in April. Mum is over the moon. Her two eldest are getting married.

There has been a two-night bombing of Berlin by the Royal Air Force. Every night we listen to the radio and pray that Les is all right. We haven't heard from him for some weeks. I imagine him sitting in a cold metal plane. The infrastructure is sparse. Only the very necessary is on board. The bombs and the fuel take most of the weight. Les and his co-pilot adjust the switches in the cockpit. Slowly, their plane rolls down the short runway. I wonder if they write messages on their loaded bombs. Messages of revenge. Messages of hate. Messages announcing their victory. What do you write to people you are just going to bomb?

The glowing sticks of the aircraft signals' officer lead my brother to his starting position. The plane's engine flares up, and the metal cabin around them trembles with the force. They are pushed back into their seats. Take-off. One plane after the other shoots off into the dark sky. They are only expected back at dawn. That is, if they make it back at all.

Lined up, they calmly travel through the pitch-black sky. Below them, nothing but deep, dark water.

They soon arrive in German airspace. Far below them they can see the city lights. Lights of homes. Lights of their enemies. The engines of their planes are almost silent. They will not be heard.

Reaching their target, they move into position and push the release buttons. Swiff, down they go. 10. 9. 8. 7. The messengers of death fall so calmly. 6. 5. 4. 3. 2. 1. Giant fireworks explode below them. It looks like a wave of fire is sweeping across the city. The wave knows no pity. Burning everything in its path. Buildings tremble and collapse. Clouds of dust and gravel ascend towards the sky.

The planes turn and make their way back to the airfield to re-arm.

We hear of the bombing on our radio. The Allies are reported to have been successful. The word 'successful' is difficult to understand when talking about bombing a city. The three of us listen to the reports. My mother cries, and my father buries his head in his hands. If only this war was over.

A week later, a letter from Les reaches us. He is okay, very tired but okay.

Mid-spring, the long awaited news reaches me. Jack has been granted a two-week leave for our marriage this June. I have booked the Registry Office, and we will have a small ceremony at the local church followed by a late lunch at the Craven Arms dining room. It will be nothing grand. We just don't have the money, and goods are scarce.

We have decided that I will stay with my parents until the war is over and Jack is safely home. The thought of having our own little place does excite me though. I catch myself studying houses. Imagining if they are for sale and if we could somehow afford one. But actually, this is a dream that will not be fulfilled. The idea is that once Jack is back I will move into his mother's house. There is more space there, and he doesn't want to leave his Mum alone.

I have decided to sew my own wedding gown. It will be a simple white dress with two layers of flounce around the seams. I have found a wonderful material in the village draper's shop. To make a perfect wedding gown will take me some time. It will help to shorten the months of waiting.

It's a beautiful June morning and I awake early. There is a lot to do. It's my wedding day. Downstairs, I can hear my Mum bustling in the kitchen. I quickly slip into my dressing gown and run downstairs. Dad is just empting his cup of black tea. "Hey love, you're up early!" he beams. "I will be out of your way in a second. Got an appointment with the barber. Want to look my best for my only daughter's wedding. Will only be giving you away once this lifetime."

"Dear, before you leave, please help us fill the bath tub, will you!" my Mum orders him. "Sure thing, don't want my girls straining their muscles," he smiles, lifting the boiling water from the fireplace and carefully pouring it into the tub.

"There you go my dear. A lovely warm bath awaits the bride," he says and kisses my forehead. "Ladies, I am off!" With the wickedest of smiles, he turns on his heel and leaves us to it.

The bath is hot and helps relax my muscles. Mum has bought a pink coloured soap smelling of fresh roses. Hoping that my fair skin will absorb the delicate smell, I rub the foam all over me. It smells divine. Closing my eyes, I imagine myself in my beautiful white gown elegantly walking out through the doors of the church into the sunlight. A small crowd of people are clapping and cheering. Rose petals are thrown into the air and gently sailing down, showering us. I am holding my just-married husband's hand. I turn to smile at him. The sunlight blinds my view. I cannot see his clean-cut features. I lift my hand to shade my eyes from the bright light. But whatever I do, his face remains unrevealed.

A single tear runs down my pale skin and drops from my chin into the tub.

This is not unseen by Mum. She always sees everything. I feel her soft hand stroke across the damp path the tear left behind on my cheek. "It's only the nerves," she calms me. Opening my eyes, I nod and try to magic a smile onto my face. Inside though, the thought of not seeing my husband's face strangely worries me.

Hours later, I live my daydream. I am wearing my beautiful handmade white gown. The soft fabric shows off my delicate curves and my slim waist. My blond curls are pinned together at the back of my head, and a small white flower decorates the bun.

Jack beams at me during the short ceremony. "You look so beautiful," he whispers to me. His eyes are glowing with love. Shyly I smile, and try to catch a glimpse of him through my lashes. He looks divine. He is wearing a dark suit with a waistcoat and a silver coloured tie. As always, his hair is neatly combed to one side. He looks happy, full of hope and love. His eyes are sparkling.

While we speak our vows, we are standing holding each other's hands, looking into our eyes, deep into our souls. It's the most intimate moment of my life. I feel I am going to burst any second due to the overflow of love and pride. Holding Jack's hands keeps me from sailing off. It keeps me here in the church, standing in front of the altar. Standing with my soon-to-be husband.

"You may kiss the bride," the parson announces. Jack pulls me towards him and his soft lips find mine. The audience around us fades. It's just him and me, united by our kiss. In the distance I can hear our wedding guests clapping. Slowly I come back to the church. Jack gently dries a tear of joy that runs down my cheek.

Outside the sun is shining. It's a wonderful late spring afternoon. A small group of guests are gathered around the church's entrance and are applauding.

I am married! I am Mrs Mary Eileen Meredith! Giddy with joy, I turn to my husband. The sun is bright and it is difficult for me to see clear features of his face. I can just see his silhouette. A wave of anxiety rushes through my body. But I don't have time to question. Jack pulls my hand and leads me through the small group of guests.

So this is it! It's what all girls dream and wait for. Their fairy tale wedding! The tall handsome prince who opens the door to the real life! Now it all begins. Or at least that is what they all think.

CHAPTER SEVEN

Well, not quite for me. I had to take a rain check for my "real life" to start. Shortly after our wedding, Jack had to go back to war. As planned, I carried on living with my parents. So not too much changed at all really. Only I was now wearing a slim sliver band. Reminding me of our fairy-tale day and our vows.

A daily routine soon gets you back into the flow. Delivering the milk, helping my mother and occasionally visiting my mother-in-law, Julie Meredith. Months pass. Seasons come and go.

From the front, we hear on our radio that the Allies are making good progress. Les has been home for a short while. Grace, now his wife, is pregnant. They are expecting their first child. Fred is doing well. He has married Joyce. They plan to stay in South Africa after the war. They sent us some pictures of their wedding day. I wish we could have been there. Joyce looked beautiful and Fred is proudly standing next to her in his Air Force uniform. I think it made my Mum a little sad not to have been part of the special day.

It's 1945, and the three of us are spending a normal evening at home. Having dinner together and then sitting around the fireplace listing to the radio. The broadcast is difficult to listen to. The crackling sound is louder than usual. The Allies have closed in on the Axis Powers, and are said to be close to the 'Führer Bunker', and consequently to Adolph Hitler.

The next morning, the breaking news is all over the newspapers. Adolph Hitler and his wife, Eva Braun, have committed suicide in the Führer Bunker. Everywhere in the village, people are standing together in huddles around radios listing to the broadcast. Has the Third Reich fallen?

Berlin is said to be in the hands of the Soviets. It can only be a matter of days before the war is declared won by the Allies.

And so it was. One week after the suicide, the war was declared over. Our relief is indescribable. At last the bombing and the killing is over. Months, no years of worrying will find their end. My love will soon come home.

Well, that's at least what you'd think when a war is over. Reality soon struck us though. Our troops need to stay abroad, secure the cities and help clear the battlefields.

We're not expecting Les or Jack to be home for at least the next 6 to 12 months. We're not expecting Fred to be back at all, as he and Joyce want to settle down in South Africa.

So once again life just carried on the normal way it always has. Only this time, we all feel more secure and confident that the good times lie in front of us.

Our family has grown. Les's little boy, John, was born over a year ago. It's wonderful having a baby in the family. Being the first Price child, John got all the attention. We challenge each other in seeing who can make him smile first. If you hold his little chubby hands, he can stand and makes his first clumsy steps. Les will be over the moon when he sees him. I cannot wait for Jack and me to have our own.

It's a chilly summer day. As usual, I have been on my milk round, and had a quick cup of tea with Edith Meredith. It was nice to hold the steaming hot tea mug. My fingers had gone all numb from carrying the cold bottles of milk all morning.

There has been no news from the army lately. We still don't know when Jack will be home. The time of waiting is slowly getting me down. What are they doing out there? Why aren't they coming home? I just don't understand. But I try not to let it show. I don't want to unnecessarily worry Edith Meredith.

After a short chat, I drive back to the dairy to unload the empty crates. "Dear, come on in with you," my Dad shouts out through the swinging doors of the dairy. "It's warm in here!" I join him and some of our co-workers in the dairy's sparse lunchroom for our break. But my packed lunch just doesn't taste so good today. Not that it's ever really a feast. It's normally just some dry bread with butter. Sometimes, if we had leftovers from dinner, we would fill our bread slices with them. As hungry as we are, we normally don't mind. But today is different. I just cannot get the bites down. Maybe it's just the chat I had with Edith Meredith that is affecting me. I try to avoid situations lately that remind me that Jack is not going to be here soon. The thoughts are always there, just not so active as when spoken about. But I couldn't really go out of the way of my mother-in-law. She is lonely in her house, and misses her son dearly.

Dad and I walk home together. "It can't be long until they send our boys back home, my dear," Dad tells me. He has noticed my troubled expression. "It has been two months since the war was declared over. I didn't think it would take this long. Why are the British cleaning-up other countries? Don't we have enough cleaning-up to do ourselves?" I ask, without expecting an answer. "Yes, it's difficult to understand isn't it? But war isn't to be understood. Don't try to work it out. It's just the way it is. We just need to carry on and make the best out of it." Dad lays his arm around my shoulders and we walk the remainder of the way in silence.

Turning into our lane, we see an army jeep parked close to our home. Two officers have stepped out of the car, and are studying a piece of paper. My Dad's hold around my shoulders tightens, and I think I can feel a shiver running through his body. The officers raise their heads and slowly walk towards our house. For a moment we stand still, frozen to the ground beneath us. On which door will they knock? Officers only ever come to homes when soldiers have fallen. Everything else you hear by telegram or post.

Holding my breath, not moving an inch, I just stand and watch. Not a muscle in my body moves. The officers are again studying their papers. They want to be sure they knock on the right door. They glance at each other. Take off their hats and tuck them under their arms. Carefully, one of them reaches out and his strong hand knocks on our door.

Mum opens. In shock, she bounces back a step. Dad releases his grip around me. Takes my hand and quickly pulls me towards our home. Not feeling if I even have legs, I let him drag me to our front door. The officers step aside to give us space to join Mum. The three of us stand still. Holding each other. Waiting for the shattering news.

"Madam, Sir, we are looking for Mary Eileen Meredith. Is she here?" the elderly officer calmly asks. I swallow. I'm not sure if I can speak. "I am Mary Eileen Meredith," I reply with a broken voice. My father's hand is squeezing mine. "Madam, we are very sorry to have to report that your husband, Jack Meredith, has fallen for his country while clearing landmines in Belgium. We cannot express how much we regret having to deliver this message to you. Especially now that the war has ended. Our country is very proud of the service Jack Meredith has rendered for peace. He will never be forgotten."

Wide-eyed and open mouthed, I listen to the officers' statement. In reality though, I'm still at their first sentence "Jack Meredith has fallen." The meaning of the words just won't go down. How is this possible? The war is over! It's only about cleaning-up and securing the cities.

Mum is standing next to me in shock. Her hands are covering her scream, dampening the sound. My father has strengthened his grip around me, holding me tight. My knees wobble. My legs give way. All goes blank. I cannot hear anything anymore. My vision tightens. It's as though I'm looking through a tunnel that is becoming narrower. The officers are out of my sight. All goes black. I am gone. Only the words "Jack Meredith has fallen" remain.

I awaken out of my dark fall. Dad has laid me on the armchair near the fireplace. It's quiet in the living room. Mum is sitting next to me, holding my hand. "Mollie?" Her voice is just a whisper. Frantically I rub my eyes trying to get my full sight back. What has happened? My thoughts are not clear. Regaining my vision I see my mother's face. It's ash grey. There are more wrinkles around her eyes than normal. Her cheeks are damp, single tears are running down her face. She is dabbing her nose with an old hankie.

Dad isn't in the room. But I believe I can hear him speaking somewhere close to the main door. My memory flashes back. The officers! They must still be outside. Dad is talking to them, but I can't make out their words.

"Mollie, love, speak to me!" my Mum takes my hand. Her thumb rhythmically strokes across the back of my hand. I open my mouth to speak, but words just won't come out. Pain rises within me. Growing rapidly, it infects cell by cell, every single one. Knowing no pity. Leaving no survivors. The inside of me shatters like glass dropped onto a stone floor. Thousand of pieces shatter in all directions. Some pieces never to be found again! I open my mouth in the hope I can release some of the pressure. But no sound will come out. It's a silent scream of immense pain. I wrap my arms around me and, with the tension of the soundless scream, bend towards my knees. A single drop falls from my eye, bounces only once off the floor before falling down again and smattering into a tiny puddle.

Later that day I wake in my bed. I am wrapped in a woolly blanket covering me from the cold draught. Lying in my bed, I hear the air whispering to me. I inhale. The air feels icy cold. I exhale. My nasal wings warm for a short moment. My breath is a misty cloud above my bed. Shivering I pull the blanket closer to my face and fall back into a dark restless sleep.

A knock at my bedroom door wakens me. It's dark outside. My mother enters the room with a steaming bowl of soup. "Mollie dear, I have made you some soup. The warmth will do you good." Carefully, she places the bowl on my bedside table and sits down on the side of my bed. Gently, she strokes some loose curls from my cheek and tugs them behind my ear. "It will take time. Let the pain out, you can't keep it all inside of you. I cannot find the right words, my love. It's not fair! War is never fair! Jack is a brave man. He has paved the way for the future generation to live in peace."

I am too numb to move, too numb to speak. Mum kisses my forehead while propping a second cushion behind my head. "That's better. Now I can help you with your soup," she smiles. "Here you go. Careful now, it's hot. It will do you good. Gosh, it's really cold in here."

I spend the rest of the night in a restless fight against the demons that are haunting me. Again and again I hold out my arms to a silhouette that appears. It's cold, and a bright light blinds me. I cannot make out the facial features. My hands just cannot touch my angel. He is out of reach.

I awake startled. Dawn is breaking. Through my bedroom window I can see the dark of the night mixing with the most beautiful blue of a new day. No sound can be heard. It's like I'm the only person awake. Dry crusts frame my eyes. My body feels drained and weak. My love is gone. My love has left me. Deep anger rises inside of me, anger against the world. Anger against feeling left alone. Anger against the sky that is showing off its most beautiful blue colours. I grab whatever is closest to me and, with a deep scream, hurl it against the wall. My bowl of cold soup slams and splitters. Thick, brown liquid splashes the pale green wallpaper. Pieces of porcelain clatter on the floor. It's quiet in my room. Except for the rhythmic dripping of soup onto the bare floorboards.

In the next-door bedroom, my mother is woken by the sound of my scream and the shattering noise of the soup bowl breaking against the wall. Quickly, she slips on her washed-out pink dressing gown and runs over to my room. "Mollie, dear, what has happened?" She gasps. Tears are pouring down my face. I cannot stop them anymore.

Mum crawls into my bed and, without any more words, just holds me tight. Lying in her arms, I crawl up and weep bitterly. My heart, my soul is torn apart. My love has gone!

I stay home over the next few days. Most of the time I don't even leave my bed. I am too torn to move. Too torn to take care of myself. Let alone think of any activity. Again and again I relive the message. "Jack Meredith has fallen." He is not coming back. The future dreams we shared will never take place. Never will our little boy run through the apple orchard and try to torment his pretty sister. The four of us will not sit in the middle of a flowery meadow and tickle each other's noses with fresh grass. Every memory of our joint dreams is a painful stab straight into my heart. Pulling me deeper and deeper into the dark.

Mum and Dad have visited Edith Meredith, Jack's Mum. I couldn't face meeting her myself. I couldn't face her pain of losing her dear son. I was too far off the cliff myself. Several consolation cards arrive, and I know I cannot hide in my room forever. A ceremony honouring Jack is to be prepared. Dad has informed me that the landmine took all of him. There are no remains to be sent home. The next day, Edith Meredith will be visiting us for lunch to discuss the ceremony details.

I awake after another night of nightmares and endless tears. My head is aching. Downstairs, I can hear Mum in the kitchen. She is preparing me a bath that I desperately need. I sit up and stretch my legs off the side of my bed. My toes reach the floorboards. The polished wood feels icy cold. Slowly, I stand on my feet and test my balance. I feel like I am standing on sheer frozen water. I take one step after the other. Holding myself tight as if my heart is made of a fragile glass. Carefully, I hold myself, making sure everything stays in one piece. Beneath me, my surface moans and the icy surface cracks. Tears spring into my eyes. I don't want to plunge. I want to be strong and I want to survive.

With the back of my hand, I wipe away the threatening tears, straighten my shoulders and take the next steps towards my bedroom door.

Downstairs, Mum is waiting for me. "Oh, my dear!" She embraces me and kisses my forehead. "Here, the hot bath will do you good. Take all the time you need!" I try to smile at her, but tears build and I quickly turn to the tub.

The hot water soothes my bones. I dive my head under the water. Down there are no sounds. Everything seems so far away. It feels like being in a cocoon. Opening my eyes, I blink and look at the world through the shimmering water. The crusts around my eyes slowly dissolve.

Lunch with Edith Meredith was very quiet. Most of the time she and I just sat and stared at our plates. The fear of losing ourselves was too present. We agreed that she would take over the organisation of the ceremony. I feel that is the only right thing to do.

After she left, I decided to sit out in the backyard for a while. Wrapped in a warm woolly jacket, I plunge into the old wicker chair. It's a crisp summer afternoon. Our garden is blooming, and the cold nights are worrying Mum. A thin layer of frost covers the dark brown soil between the plants. Mum has scattered some leftovers for the birds. As I quietly sit and watch the garden, a little robin redbreast lands and picks the dry bread. He seems to see me. Now and then he looks me in the eye and chirps. It's as though he is telling me to stay put. Kind of "Don't move. I'm hungry!" Leaning my head against the wall, I relax for the first time since receiving the news.

CHAPTER EIGHT

Nearly a year has gone since Jack passed away, and we are again in the middle of spring. The winter snow has melted and our backyard is starting to grow. Mum is busy everyday getting her plants ready. A lot of the time I'm out with her, and help sowing seeds and preparing stems for the runner vegetables to climb up. The activity does me good. It takes my mind off everything else. As silly as it sounds, the work allows my mind to go blank and have time to rest while I am digging in the garden. It's like watching birds feed. In that special moment all the hundreds of thoughts racing through your head, nagging you, will be gone for a few seconds. Giving your mind the space to step out of the complicated structures of "ifs" and "when's." A moment of peace!

Most men are now back from the war. Reunited with their loved ones. I've managed to hold on to my milk round so far. But, sooner or later, I will have to make way for family fathers in need of a job. My plan is to go back into needle-work. Money is still very tight, and goods are hard to get. Due to this, there is currently no large demand. Everyone tries to get by with what they have. But I've been able to alter the odd dress or trouser seam, and hope to slowly build on this.

I haven't really kept much contact with Jack's mother, Edith Meredith. She always kept very much to herself and we did the same. I would occasionally see her on my milk round, and she would offer me a cup of tea. She organized a nice ceremony for Jack, and has hung a plaque on one of the apple trees. The orchard meant so much to him. I'm sure he's pleased.

The bleeding of my wounds caused by the sudden loss has stopped. A thick crust had dried on top. Now and then, if I move too quickly, the crust tears slightly. Mostly leaving me with silent tears at night that my cushion swallows. At not even 30 years of age, I am a widow. I never even lived with my husband. But at least it was only me that was left. Many other women my age were left with children to bring up by themselves.

One spring afternoon, there's a knock at our door. Mum and I are busy working in the garden. Mum brushes her hands and makes her way to the door. It's a bright sunny day, and I feel quite sticky. My forehead is itching, and I wipe it with my forearm. Only to notice afterwards that I am covered with dust up to my elbows. "I must be a fine sight!" I say out loud to myself, and shake my head. "I think you look like a real country beauty!" A deep voice comes back from the kitchen door. Surprised, I turn and see Mum and a man entering the garden. The man has a happy face and is grinning from one ear to the other. He has straight blonde hair and is tall with a slim build. "Mollie, dear, this is Bill, Bill Cooke. He's just back from the war and needs some of his trousers altered. He got your address from a neighbour," Mum explains. Getting to my feet, I brush the brown dust from my skirt. "Sure, I can get them done for you," I shyly smile. "Just give me a minute to get myself sorted." "No worries, I'm in no rush," Bill drops himself into the wicker chair.

I quickly rush upstairs to my bedroom. I must look a right sight. Glancing in the mirror I realize I have a brown streak all over my forehead. I dab my face with a flannel and some cold water. Comb my hair into shape and change my clothes. I fetch my sewing kit out of my wardrobe. Flustered as I am, I lose half of the contents while pulling it out of the corner. "Am I nervous?" I ask myself, kneeling down to pick up the escaped pieces.

Downstairs, Mum and Bill have seated themselves in the armchairs and are drinking a cup of tea. The atmosphere is calm and peaceful. "What would you like changed, Bill?" I ask, entering the room. "Well, I've lost some weight during the war days. Could you tighten these two a little?" Bill points to two pairs of brown cotton trousers. "I would like to be able to let them out again once I'm back to my normal size," he adds with a wicked grin.

"That won't be a problem. Let me take your measurements. It's best if you stand up over here." I gesture to the open space between kitchen and dinner table. Measuring his waist and hip, I realize that he indeed does have a slim frame. But he feels strong and grounded. Somebody who knows where he belongs!

"Right, that's it. That's all I need. I can get them done by tomorrow late afternoon if that's okay with you." "That's a shame. I was just getting into this!" Bill smiles his wicked smile. "Tomorrow will be fine. I'll come after work. Is around 5 p.m. okay?" He asks. "Yes, of course, I'll see you then," I smile.

After Bill has left, Mum and I finish up in the garden. We are both smiling. What a nice surprise!

The next day, Bill is punctual to the minute. At exactly 5 p.m., he knocks on our door. I give him some space to try his newly altered trousers in my bedroom. It doesn't take long and he is back downstairs. "That's a fine job you've done, Mollie! Thank you." "You're welcome. I'm glad they fit. Would you like a cup of tea?" I shyly ask. "That would be nice," Bill beams at me. We sit and chat for over an hour. Bill is a very calm and interesting man, with many stories to tell. We talk about the war and how everything is changing. Bill has been lucky to find work as a mechanic in a local Church Stretton garage. He likes the village and hopes to be able to settle down there one day. It's starting to get dark outside. Mum and Dad arrive home and sit with us. "Bill, would you join us for dinner?" Mum asks. "It will be nothing fancy, but something that will warm our tummies". Bill looks happily surprised by the offer. "I would very much enjoy that if I am really no burden?" "No, don't be daft. We would love to hear some more of your stories," Mum smiles, walking over to the kitchen.

The four of us spend a joyful evening together. Bill tells us stories from the war. It all sounds so light and harmless. Filled with victory and new experiences. Bill tells us how he single-handed liberated Lille from the Nazis. He was the first to walk into the town, and was greeted by a cheering parade of civilians. The streets quickly filled with people cheering their saviour. "I never felt so important as at that moment," he tells us with sparkling eyes of joy. "And it was grand in Falaise. After surviving D-Day, we, the Allies, were able to break the German lines. But another fight awaited us in Falaise. After 10 days of relentless fighting, we were able to liberate the town.

"On the 11th night, Danny, John and I were on night patrol. The town was quiet and it didn't look like we would have a lot to do. You know, we just make sure everything stays calm!"

"So we were walking down an alley when we noticed a light burning down in a basement. Just as we were getting down on our knees trying to peer through the blurred glass window, two locals opened the door to the basement. I don't know who was more shocked!" Bill laughs. "They quickly recognized that we were from the right side. They seemed very excited and were talking all sorts. I didn't understand a word. They grabbed us by the sleeves and, before I knew what was going on, the three of us were standing in a small stone-walled cellar room."

"They didn't have much light down there. Just some candles and the embers of their tobacco lit up the room. It was smoky and damp. Seven or eight men with bushy eyebrows and moustaches were sitting around an old wooden table. Smoking and playing some card game I've never seen before."

"They were all talking at the same time and frantically waving their arms. Raising their fists to the ceiling, making victory signs and laughing. Their cheeks were red with excitement. They had wide sparkling eyes, and were clapping each other on the shoulders. We were quickly sat down and given a glass each. Out of a box in the corner, they fetched a bottle of what they called Calvados. Our glasses were filled to the brim. We toasted victory and a quick end to the war."

It was lovely feeling the amber-coloured firewater warm my bones." He smiled with a dreamy expression on his face. "It was the first time I had tasted Calvados. If I understood their English properly, they were not only celebrating their newly-found freedom, but also that they could start producing delicious brandy again. We stayed there all night. Smoking and enjoying our warming drinks with our new French friends. That was a night!" He sighed, reliving the experience.

Bill's stories were stories of the better side of war. The kind of stories we hadn't heard too much about, and let us hope that Les, Fred and Jack have also made such encounters.

Riveted by his stories, we didn't notice the time fly by.

"Well, it's getting late. I'd better be on my way. Got to be back at work early tomorrow and I don't want to make a bad appearance. I've had a wonderful time. Thank you very much for the dinner!" Bill sincerely thanks the three of us. Stands-up and neatly lifts his chair back under the dinner table. "You are very welcome. It was a nice surprise. You are always welcome," Mum says, standing up and stretching her hand out to Bill. Dad and I join her, and accompany Bill to the door. Before leaving, Bill turns towards me. "Mollie, would you like to visit Church Stretton some day?" It's a lovely village and I can borrow the garage's car to drive you there." Mum and Dad discreetly vanish back into the living room. "That's very nice of you. Maybe one day," I reply, not really knowing what to say. "Good!" He smiles his wicked smile. "Let's do that one day! My lady," he bows his head, turns and walks down our lane. I wave goodbye and watch him vanish in the dark. I need to sort my thoughts!

Later that night, lying in my bed, I stare at the ceiling looking for answers. Should I be going for an outing with a man? In my mind, I recite my vows from memory. Is this the way it should be? For the remainder of my life, lying in bed alone at my parents' home with only my vows? I have just turned 30. What happened to my plans for my life? Wasn't it all only just supposed to start? I relive the dreams of Jack and myself. A family and a home of our own filled with happiness. As my imaginary film of "how it should be" plays in front of my eyes, I feel my heart crack. My eyes water and, slowly, one tear after the other escapes and rolls down the side of my face. Turning on my side, I hold myself and let my tears silently soak into my pillow. I just don't feel ready to let go and start anew.

This night I dream of Jack. It's our wedding day. We are standing in a plain church holding each other's hands. My white gown softly flows down my body meeting the grey stone floor. Jack is dressed in a smart dark suit. Looking into each other's eyes, we are looking deep into our souls. It's a warm day. Sun is shining through the stained-glass windows. Reflecting a rainbow of colours onto the bare walls. There's only him and me in the church. Soft, heavenly music raises and drifts through the room. We speak our vows. The sunlight strengthens and the rainbow of colours intensifies.

It's so bright. It's blinding. I can't hold eye contact. For only a split second I squint. When I open my eyes again, Jack is gone.

I am standing alone in the church with only my bridal bouquet in my hand. Outside, a rising wind is howling, banging against the windows. It sounds like a storm is building up. The church doors give way. Swing open and bang against the walls, leaving white dust falling to the ground. A gush of air storms down the aisle accompanied by wildly dancing orangey-brown leaves.

Everything calms down. The wind is gone. The storm has died down. The autumn leaves slowly sail down onto the grey stone ground and gather around my feet. They have paved a colourful carpet down the aisle leading out into the fresh air.

Tightly holding my bridal bouquet in my hands, I make my way to the entrance. The carpet of leaves feels soft beneath my step and rustles quietly. The warm colours dance around the bottom of my gown like little fairies playing. Standing beneath the arch of the church's door I shade my eyes from the sun. I can see for miles!

The next morning I awake with a clear mind. Downstairs, I sit with Mum and enjoy a hot cup of tea. "That was nice yesterday, wasn't it?" My Mum tries to casually remark. But it's obviously not meant casually at all. It's all questioning. "It was, wasn't it? I enjoyed the stories. It opened a new view on things." Mum is carefully watching me with a scolding look. It's not the information she wants. It's not what she wants to talk about. I roll my eyes and pull a pouting face. "Mum, not even a year has passed. Don't you think it's a bit early?" I ask her, looking for reassurance. "Mollie, you're not getting any younger. Really, how many nice, down-to-earth and unmarried Shropshire lads do you expect to meet?" I stare at her, amazed by her words. Is it that simple?

"Love, I have seen how much you have suffered during the past year. But Jack has gone. You are still young. If you want to get something out of life you need to move on. You are not helping anybody living here with us as a sad widow. Don't get me wrong, I love having you here, but I wish more for you in life. Les and Grace are already expecting their second little one. And Fred and Joyce down in South Africa their first. I would like to see my Mollie with a little one, one day," she sadly smiles at me. "That was the plan, Mum. Jack and I wanted two of our own. First a boy and then a sweet little girl. But that dream was taken from us," I say with low voice, while feeling the table's surface with my finger. I pretend to study the structure of the wood, and this way avoid her eye contact. I don't want her to see my watery eyes. But my mother never misses anything. "Love, I don't want to push you. Just take the thought and let it settle. See what it does with you," she soothingly tells me, while gently squeezing my hand.

I follow her advice and try and imagine how it could be and how it makes me feel. I enjoy dreaming of possible situations. Imagining myself doing this and that. What I would wear, what Bill would be like and our home. Maybe I should have a look at this Church Stretton place. Just to get an idea. But how will I ever meet Bill again? Will I ever meet him again? I don't have any of his home details. The only thing I really know is that he works for a garage in Church Stretton. How many garages could there be? I could check the telephone directory. We have a telephone book of the area downstairs, next to the telephone. I decide I will just have a look, so that I know.

Going through the directory I soon find the Church Stretton pages. There is only one garage. It's the Morris garage. I make a note of the address and telephone number, just in case. Or should I just call? Get it done with! Take advantage of the quiet moment.

Before rethinking what I am doing, I put the telephone receiver to my ear and dial the noted digits. God, what am I doing? But I don't have time to quickly drop the receiver back onto the hook. "Morris Garage. How can I help you?" A deep, grumbly voice asks. "Ah, hmm, could I speak to Bill Cooke please?" "Just a moment ma'am. Bill!" He shouts out loud. "There's a call for you!"

I hear the receiver drop on a hard surface and the sound of heavy boots walking off into the distance. My heart is pounding. I fear that it can be heard outside of my body too. The line crackles. "Bill Cooke speaking. How can I be of service?" I immediately recognize his soft, patient voice. "Ah, Bill, it's me. Mollie, ahh Mollie Price." I have started using Price again. It saves some questions, and as Jack and I never lived together I kind of always stayed a Price everywhere. "You had dinner with us a few days ago," I add. For a second the line is quiet. "Mollie, what a nice surprise! I wasn't expecting to hear you today," he replies after a short break. "How are you doing?" He asks kindly. "Thank you, I'm fine. I was just thinking of Church Stretton. I would be curious to see the village. So if you have time we could do the "one-day", for example next Saturday or Sunday?"

"It would be an honour Mollie! I'd love to show you the place. It's a lovely village. Small and neat! So how about I pick you up on Saturday after lunch? Let's say 2.30 p.m.?"

"2:30 p.m. this Saturday! That suits me perfectly, thank you. So I will see you then," I nervously reply. "See you Saturday, Mollie. I'm looking forward to it." We both hang up, and I release my long-held breath.

"What have I done?" My conscience asks me. From the other side of my mind, my goddess smiles triumphantly. "It's too late now. Done is done." I discharge both by reminding myself it's only for research. To see what the village does to me. So I can imagine more clearly how it potentially could feel.

It's Saturday lunchtime. The three of us are having a cold lunch. Some bread with cheese and pickled onions my mother made. It's delicious but I am just too nervous to eat. The bread is hard to swallow. I can feel my parents watching me. Oh, I'll be glad when we have finished lunch and I can vanish to my room for some quiet moments.

"Mollie, would you like to borrow my new flowery dress? It should fit you nicely with a ribbon around the waist. What do you think?" Mum kindly asks me. Astonished, I look at her. "The outing is only research, Mum. You know, seeing how it could feel. I will be fine with one of my dresses. Thank you!" Mum looks disappointed. "How will you really know how it feels if you don't try properly?" She counters. Trust her to find such a reply, I grumble to myself. "I will be fine Mum, let me first see what I have upstairs," I quickly reply, and start carrying the empty plates to the kitchen sink. I need to get out of this discussion.

Upstairs in my room, I look through my wardrobe and pick a pale pink skirt and off-white cardigan. That will look pretty, but still casual.

Looking at myself in the mirror, I decide to pep up the combination just a little with a silky scarf. There we go. Very researchy!

There is a knock at the door downstairs. Bill has arrived, punctual as usual. He has borrowed the Morris' garage car. It's a simple black car with advertising signs on the doors. Driving down the narrow country lanes, Bill tells me all about his work as a mechanic. He enjoys fixing cars. Getting his hands dirty and making cars purr again. Morris' is a family business. Morris senior and junior both work for the garage. The atmosphere is pleasant, and they spend lunch together, sitting on boxes, eating their sandwiches.

The drive to Church Stretton only takes 10 minutes. The village is surrounded by green, rural-looking hills. Just like Strefford. There is a market square and some nice look-ing shops. The town centre is not too busy. Some locals are running errands, chatting on the pavement or having tea at the local tea shop.

Bill shows me a small gate that leads to St. Laurence's parish church. The church stands in the middle of an old graveyard. Four small paths lead through soft green grass up to the sandy-grey coloured church. Around the graveyard, a stone fence protects the small area. On top of the church's steeple the English flag is proudly waving in the soft spring breeze. The white and red colour stands out beautifully against the clear blue sky. The church and its surrounding are picturesque.

Bill guides me up the little path, past the church and out through the gate on the other side. "Up this street and to the right and we are at the garage. I'd like to show you where I work," Bill beams. The area is quiet. Lots of little cottages line the street. On one side, the row of houses ends and a wide gravel path leads to an open green space. A heavy country gate separates the gravel from a path leading up the hill to a wood. It looks just like home.

"Would you like to have a walk up?" Bill asks, realising my interest. "Yes, that would be nice," I reply, with sparkling eyes. The gravel stones grind beneath our feet. I am glad that I am wearing good shoes. The wooden gate is as heavy as it looks, but Bill holds it open for me. Together, we wander up the path. Left and right from us there are open green spaces. Some white sheep have noticed us. After some curious studying, they decide to run off to a safer spot. At the entrance to the wood there is a second wooden gate. A little bench captures my eye. "Let's sit down for a moment!" I say, pointing to the bench. "This reminds me of my childhood. I love the Shropshire hills. My brothers and I used to be up the hills or roaming the woods every possible minute. We would always be getting into trouble with Mum." I smile and take a deep breath. The smell of fresh grass fills my nostrils.

The view from the bench is breathtaking. You can see across the village's rooftops. St. Laurence's steeple and the English flag waving in the glorious blue sky. In the distance, more green hills follow each other for miles. The picture is peaceful. It just feels right sitting here.

Later that Saturday, Bill proudly shows me the garage. The garage is like a spacious hangar. Around the grey walls there are old metal cabinets and sets of drawers. They look like they desperately need a clean. There are lots of oily looking bottles and paint tubs on top of the drawers. In the middle of the room, there is a car lift that they use to do work on the underside of the cars. The hangar smells of melted metal and paintwork. Not really the things that interest me, but I let him show me them all. He is so proud. His position as a mechanic is the first real job he has had, if you don't count the war service. At the back of the hangar there is a little glass cabinet. Inside, there is an old wooden desk and two simple looking chairs with black leather backing. The leather looks dry and there are some thin rips held together with sellotape. A black telephone is sitting between piles of paper on the wooden desk. I blush seeing it and imagine Bill sitting on one of the chairs in a blue overall. His legs crossed, leaning back and looking through the glass window, watching his colleagues work. Luckily the garage is gloomy, and I don't think that Bill has noticed my change of colour.

Driving back to Strefford, we talk about our childhood. Bill grew up with two brothers in a small country village nearby called Clee Hill. His father worked in the farming industry and his mother took care of their home. It was rough with two brothers. They were always up to all sorts. Getting into scuffles with each other. Chasing sheep up the hills, tripping over stones and ripping their trousers, which got them into even more trouble at home. What he loved most was catching fish with his bare hands. His Dad taught him this. I smile remembering how Les loved to do this too, and how proud he was to spend time with Dad.

He lost contact to his brothers during the war. He's back with his parents now until he has earned enough to buy his own place.

We have arrived at my parent's house. The lights are lit and I am feeling hungry. "Bill, would you like to join us for dinner?" I ask him, hoping to hear some more of his stories. "That is a lovely offer, but I don't want to be a burden for your mother again. They aren't expecting me and I don't want you all to go short." Before Bill can finish his sentence, the door to our house opens and my Mum pops her head out. "Mollie, Bill, you are just on time! I was hoping you would be back soon. I have prepared dinner. The two of you are going to join us, aren't you?" Mum is all smiley and bright. She planned this, and I am glad she did!

"Edith, that is very generous of you. If you were counting with me, I cannot say no. I wouldn't want any food to go to waste." Bill returns, while opening the car door on my side to let me out.

The four of us spend another joyful evening together. It feels like we have known each other forever. Bill is warm and sincere. He doesn't take anybody's place. He is the missing piece, a calming influence that fills us with hope.

CHAPTER NINE

It's a warm Friday afternoon, unusually warm actually for an October day. I'm in my bedroom preparing for my second big day. This time though, it will be less formal than the first time. Bill and I have decided to only have a registry office wedding. Yes, that's right. Bill and I are getting married.

We enjoyed a lovely summer together. Spending a lot of time getting to know Church Stretton. We imagined being part of the village. Shopping at the local market, spending occasional nights out at the pub. We even spotted a tiny one-up one-down third of a cottage in Church Street. It's only a two-minute walk away from Morris' garage. Our hopes are high that the local bank will grant us a mortgage.

We spoke a lot about the war. Even about Jack. Bill was also part of the KSLI, the Kings Shropshire Light Infantry. They weren't part of the same troop, but Bill had heard about Jack and the devastating accident after the war had ended. I was surprised how understanding he was, and that I was able to speak with him about my fears. He never tried to take Jack's place and I didn't feel pressured. Everything was given the necessary space.

Our courting was different from what I had experienced with Jack. Not that it wasn't romantic or exciting. That it was! Bill is very charming and warm hearted. He is a real gentleman, and I feel protected and safe when I'm with him. It felt more grown-up, if I can put it that way. My time with Jack was somehow unreal. We didn't spend much time together. We spent a lot of time writing to each other, reading about our individual dreams. But not much talking about them. Not spending hours talking and understanding details, allowing my mind to create my own imagination. If you make-up your reality it's always perfect, because your mind will make it perfect for you. But would it be this way in real life?

This is what was different with Bill. Bill and I would speak for hours. I knew exactly what he meant, and so did he. Being able to spend a lot of time together also allowed us to actively create our future. We were happy together. Enjoyed the peaceful moments, the rural hills, the trees in the wood, the pond and, most of all, our future home, Church Stretton.

So I'm sitting in my bedroom. I have hand-sewed myself a two-piece suit. The fabric is a pale pink, light wool material. It feels lovely and soft. The skirt is a straight cut, and ends just at my knees. The jacket closes at the front with two matching pink buttons. Luckily enough, I was able to find a pretty hat and some shiny black shoes at a store in Shrewsbury. They fit me perfectly. It is still difficult to obtain goods, and food is still mainly rationed. But we believe we can slowly see the light at the end of the tunnel. When we were children, my parents taught us to be economical with money. We never waste food, and we always try to grow or make our own to help with the situation.

"Mollie, dear, are you ready?" my Mum calls me through the door. It doesn't take a minute, and her head is poking through the doorway. She is very excited. She and Dad love Bill. Plus, this is the first wedding when all her children, and even the three grandchildren, will be present.

Les and Grace are here with their two boys, John and Robert. Robert is only tiny, a couple of months old. Fred and Joyce have flown over from South Africa. It's the first time Fred has been back since the start of the war. Their little girl, Barbara, is with them. She is just starting to walk and is constantly exercising her first words. The words are like "Mummy", "Daaaddy", "look", "me hungry" and "miau". Obviously, everybody is trying to teach her something new to say. She is a happy little girl. Always smiling and showing off her beautiful brown curls.

"I've got my blush with me. Here you go. Oh, your suit looks beautiful, dear!" Mum plunges down on the end of my bed. She is also wearing a two-piece suit. A beautiful navy blue pencil skirt and matching jacket. It looks lovely with her neatly combed brown hair and sparkling green eyes. "Thank you, Mum. I'm very pleased the way it turned out." I gently smooth the skirt down the sides and turn to each side in front of the mirror. Yes, I'm very pleased indeed.

"Well, I shouldn't be keeping you too long dear. I will be downstairs with Dad, waiting for you. Les and Fred will be meeting us with their families at the registry office. So see you in a few minutes." She kisses my forehead, holding me gently. She looks so happy. Her eyes are dazzling. I haven't seen her like this for years. Light really seems to be waiting at the end of a long tunnel. Before I know, she is off and I am alone in my bedroom.

I breathe deeply and, for a moment, enjoy the peace. I can see the greenest hills through my bedroom windows. The sun is shining and it's a bright day. Gazing up the hills, I watch the little white spots wandering from one feeding spot to the other. For a moment, I'm back in my childhood days. Standing in my room with an air pencil. What secret message would I discover today? I draw from one white spot to the other. The lines are very straight. They seem to be standing in a perfect square. Oh, and there's another one right up the top. I can just make it out. I join the upper two ends of my square with the higher single spot. There I go. My picture is finished. My hills have shown me a house, my home. Secretly smiling at my discovery, I apply a little blush to my cheeks. What a promising sign.

Standing in front of the mirror, I straighten my skirt one more time. Carefully I pin my hat to my hair and slip into my shoes. Time to go.

Dad has borrowed a car from the dairy owner, so we have our own transportation. Our families are already waiting at the registry office. Les, Grace and their two boys. Fred and Joyce with little Barbara. Bill's parents and his two brothers with their wives. We are quite a group. At the front, Bill is standing and beaming by the car. He is wearing a dark brown suit. A little pink flower is looped through the top buttonhole of his jacket. The flower matches the ones in my bridal bouquet. It looks very elegant. His blond hair is, as usual, combed back, slightly to one side.

As soon as our car stops, Bill rushes over to open the car door for me. Taking my hand, he helps me out of the back seat. His hands are warm and feel strong. He pulls me towards him and lays his arm around me. His eyes are glowing with love. He strokes my cheek with one hand. Gently tilts my head back and places his lips on mine. A bundle of butterflies awaken inside of me. The prickling feeling of their wings brushing against me rushes through my whole body.

"Easy now, you're not married yet!" My Dad warns with a wicked smile. Both of us blush and straighten our suits.

Inside the registry office, we are led to a wood-panelled room. Bill and I are seated in two single chairs in front of a dark wooden desk. The desk is decorated with a beautifully flower arrangement that gives the room a ceremonial touch. Scattered around the room behind us there are several padded chairs and one large sofa where our family members can take a seat. Once the room has calmed down, the registrar starts speaking. She welcomes us all to their offices on this wonderful day for this beautiful occasion. Carrying on, she talks a lot in metaphors that I like very much. Pictures help me understand her words and memorise what she says. There's a lot about a new joint beginning. We are like Phoenix rising from the ashes. Flapping our wings, seeing the dark ashes of the past loosen and fall. Turning us into a white dove, ready to fly. To fly out into a new joint future, where everything is possible, everything is light and clear.

She also talks a lot about love and marriage. Being together. Standing for each other. Being our lover, our partner and our bastion of calm. Inside, I feel my nervousness growing. I know the moment of our vows is close. Nervously, I knot my fingers into each other on my lap. I wish I could just go out for a moment, calm myself and then come back again. I would feel better. But how would that sound if I were to request a bathroom break in the middle of our wedding ceremony? Sometimes my thoughts seem ridiculous. My thinking makes me smirk inwardly. As if he sensed my conflict, Bill reaches over, and his hand captures mine. He feels warm and secure. His touch stabilises me. Inside of me, my cells stop bouncing all over the place.

The registrar requests us to stand and turn to each other. Doing this, Bill never lets go of my hand. His eyes never leave mine. He is looking deep into my eyes, deep into my soul and I am doing the same. I can see only love. Deep love surrounded by never-ending security, warmth and a home forever. I know he will always be by my side. Never pressure me, never take my space and always support who I am. A rush of love and an unbelievable feeling of happiness flows through me. My heart is close to bursting. I know he will be the one that will make me happy for the remainder of my life. We quietly speak our vows, never losing eye contact. We slip on each other's rings and seal the ceremony with a kiss. We are married. We are Mr and Mrs Cooke. Our small crowd claps and cheers.

We have booked our wedding reception in the dining area of the Ragleth Inn in Church Stretton. Our small group spends a quiet but lovely evening together. Soft music plays in the background from the radio, and the atmosphere is happy and light. Our meal is crowned with a three-storey sponge cake soaked in orange liquor, covered with white icing and decorated with sweet purple flowers. It tastes delicious.

A saxophone playing a melancholy tune on the radio captures our attention. A deep voice joins in and sings about divine love. The tune is heavenly, and carries me away to a pink, cotton-wool-padded place full of love.

A tap on my shoulder awakens me. Bill is standing next to me, looking down with warm sparkling eyes. "Mrs Cooke, will you dance with me?" he whispers, holding out his hand for mine. Glowing with pride, I discharge the thought that I am not a passionate dancer. I am just too happy to even think of something like that. Standing to my feet, I notice that the sparkling wine we have been drinking has done its work. I feel a little giddy. Bill puts his strong arm around me and leads me to an open space in the room. He draws me close into his embrace and we move smoothly across the floor. Our bodies melt together joined by the sweet tone of the saxophone and the deep singing voice. The world around us evaporates. It's just the two of us, elegantly swirling through the room. The air heats up with everlasting love. It's touchable. It tickles my skin and warms my heart. A tear of happiness makes its way down my cheek and reaches my lips. The salty taste awakens my senses. The moment is real. I am alive and full of love. I have found my place, and the future stands wide open. My love is home.

A week later the happy news reaches us. The bank will grant us a mortgage. We can buy our own home! Our tiny one-up one-down is part of a cottage on 18 Church Street in Church Stretton. The cottage is separated into three little homes. Our's is the one on the left side. The other two house parts are lived in by elderly ladies without family. It's the first own home for both of us. Even though the mortgage scares us, we feel so proud and blessed by God.

Downstairs, we have our living-diner room and an open kitchen. The back door leads out to a thin patch of land and the bathroom facilities. Upstairs is our bedroom. To save some money, my parents have let me have some of my bedroom furniture to start off with. For the living room, we have bought two comfy armchairs to rest in. We found a dark wood table with four matching chairs in the Church Stretton antique market, and a mix of pretty plates. Choosing the plates was my highlight. I love pretty china!

Sadly, as a result of the move, I have had to give up my milk round. "Mollie the Milk" now belongs to the past. I am carrying on with my needlework, for which I am getting better and better known. It has become a nice additional income, and allows me to work from home. I have always enjoyed being at home. Especially now, having our own first four walls. Bill and I enjoy our weekends working in the garden. Next spring, we want to see our own vegetables sprout.

The elementary school is just across the road from our home. To help pay back our mortgage I have been able to find a part-time job as a school cleaning help. I was well taught by Mum how to keep a clean home, and it's nice to get to know the locals through the school. Within no time at all, the picturesque village has become our home and we feel as snug as a bug in a rug.

The next summer, our piece of luck feels endless. Not only is our garden getting on well, we are also expecting our first baby. My little bump makes me so proud that I could cry every time I think of the little wee thing growing inside me. The first weeks of feeling sick have luckily past, and I now feel happy and fit. I am carrying on with my work at the school for the time being, and the needlework is no bother. I have an obsession with sewing little baby outfits and cot blankets. Our wardrobe is growing weekly. This Saturday, we are going to town to find a matching cot for our bedroom. Excitedly, I awake early, too early to wake Bill. Lying in our bed, I stare at the ceiling. With my eyes, I follow the pattern of the white paint. The curves the paintbrush left behind are soft and seem never ending. I imagine filling every paintbrush bristle with another colour. A flamboyant, endless rainbow appears on our ceiling. The curves make me feel that I could slide down the rainbow and go up the other side. A rainbow caterpillar! I imagine our child playing. Bill and I are waiting at the lower curves. Waiting to catch our little one who is sliding down the colourful rays. Our child's blonde hair is softly blowing in the wind, and the air is filled with the giggling and squealing of a child's joy. The rainbow caterpillar suddenly starts to move its body. Slowly, it sways its tummy up and down. Bouncing our little one gently into the air and catching it again like a soft trampoline. The joy is deafening. Happiness overcomes me and I burst into laughter.

Next to me, Bill is bounced out of his sleep by my giggling. He turns and looks at me through sleepy eyes. "Mollie, what's so funny? Are you dreaming?" His eyes are automatically closing again while he wraps his arm around me and pulls me close to his warm body. Lying in his soft embrace, I close my eyes and thank the rainbow caterpillar. Smiling from one ear to the other, I doze in my husband's arms. Later that day, we find a perfect wooden cot. Once home again, I decide to paint a chubby rainbow caterpillar on the cot's headpiece.

We have decided that I will give birth to our baby at home, in our upstairs bedroom. I have never liked being in hospitals. They are so bare and cold. It doesn't feel like the right surroundings for our baby to come into the world. It's the middle of March, and terribly cold. We have had some snow, and I am glad to have a reason not to go out. My tummy is massive. I feel just as tall, if you can talk about tall in my case, as wide. With little kicks, our baby is letting me know non-stop that she is ready to come. This is making me run to the freezing cold bathroom in the back more often than I like. Every night, I lie in bed and enjoy the routine of Bill gently creaming my tummy with his warm hands. We can see the little ones feet and fists whenever it makes itself seen by kicking or punching against my tummy. Our eyes water at the miracle.

On a Tuesday, 16.03.1948, early in the morning, my waters break. Too shocked to move, we both just stand there looking at each other. "Bill, you should call the doctor," I order, getting my senses back together. Bill still looks frozen to the floor. As if he has forgotten where our telephone is or even that we have a telephone. "Bill! You need to call the doctor!" I repeat with a more strict tone. "Oh yes, yes, of course! I'm on my way. You should lie down. Shall I help you?" He asks me with scattered words. "No, no. You just call the doctor. I will be fine. It doesn't hurt!" Well, that was said a bit too early.

Later on that morning, I am lying in bed in a puddle of sweat. My face is distorted with pain. A midwife is constantly dabbing my forehead. Every time a contraction begins, she calmly breathes with me. "You are close, Mollie. Your baby is ready to come. When the next labour starts, you will have to push as much as you can. Do you understand?" She is looking at me with a strict expression. I nod, too afraid to disagree. And I want this to be done. I want to see my baby and I want this ripping pain to stop.

One more time I sink back into my cushion. Close my eyes and gather all my energy. Deep inside, I can feel the build-up of the next contraction. I don't fight it. I just let it happen. Here we go. The pain grows. I keep my eyes closed and lean forward towards my knees. My teeth grit, and my hands form fists. A loud groan whistles through my teeth. The midwife is standing ready at the bottom of my bed. "That's good. You are doing well. I can see the baby's head. One more push, Mollie!" She encourages me. I use all my reserves. Press my eyes together even more. My back bends with the pressure, and my head touches my knees. Raising my fists to the air, I scream as I feel something slump between my legs. Grasping for air, I lean back onto my cushion. My scream is followed by an innocent, light, weighted cry. Our child is born.

The midwife calls Bill to cut the umbilical cord. He looks a little shocked on seeing all the blood. But the amazement of our newly-born and his duty as father overweighs. After the ritual is done, she wraps our baby in a soft towel and hands me the little bundle. "Mollie, here is your daughter!" Bill plunges down next to me on our bed. We just sit and stare at this little person. Our little girl is here. Her little hands are stiffly sticking out of the towel. Bill counts her fingers. "All ten are there! She's perfect!" Tears of thankfulness run down our faces. She is so beautiful. I cannot take my eyes off her. I feel so blessed. So full of endless love for this little person. I will never let her go.

That evening, holding our little girl in our arms, we decide to call her Susan. Susan Mary Cooke.

It's unimaginable how a child of your own changes your life. On the one side there are the sleepless nights and the tired mornings after. The constant nappy changing and the endless crying. But all is immediately forgotten as soon as we look into our little girl's eyes. We only want to hold her tight to our heart. Watching her fall asleep in our arms is heavenly. In those moments she is so peaceful and full of trust towards her parents. Whatever we do, it's always also for her now. She fully relies on us and it's our highest priority to make sure she's safe.

Our tiny home has become really cramped with the three of us. We are in need of more space. Our neighbours, the two elderly ladies, have both decided to sell each of their cottage thirds and move to a nursing home. This is our chance to take over the whole cottage and realise our dream home. We are short of money though, and it worries us a lot to be in so much debt with the bank. The economy is recovering, but only slowly. And there's now the three of us. But if we don't take the other two cottage parts, we don't know what will happen. Both are in desperate need of renovation, and we're not sure if a buyer will be found.

We decide to go forward and realise our dreams. The bank and the Morris' garage grant us a loan. In order to start paying back the loans quickly, Bill takes on a second job as the school bus driver, and occasionally drives the hearse to funerals.

Our home turns into a construction site. First the two women's homes are turned into one. We decide to have the main entrance to the house set traditionally in the middle. Coming in through the main door, we will have a cloakroom and a spacious landing with a staircase to the upper floor. Downstairs to the right, there is a sitting room with a large storage area in the back and the entrance to the cellar. The kitchen with pantry and living room will be built on the left lower side of the house. From the kitchen, we plan a direct access through a glass extension with a small toilet to the large garden. The glass extension will be our school for baby plants, and a winter home for the more sensitive greenery.

Upstairs, our bedroom will be on the right side, and we will have a small guest room at the back. Susan's room will be on the left, where our bedroom is now. I like the thought that she will be able to see green hills through her bedroom window in the same way that I could in my childhood days.

But the most exciting room will be in the middle of the upper floor. Our first indoor bathroom will be installed at the end of the staircase. A bathroom with a real flushable toilet and a built-in bathtub. No more freezing outside and washing myself in a zinc tub in the kitchen. I can't wait.

While our rebuilding was going on, our family grew some more. My brother Les and his wife Grace have had their third child. Little Pat was born shortly after our Susan. Les and Grace are over the moon to finally have a girl after two boys. In South Africa, my youngest brother Fred and his wife Joyce have adopted a little boy called Glyn. Now their daughter Barbara finally has a brother to play with. The contact to our siblings had loosened quite a lot. I guess we were all just too caught-up with our own lives. I see my Mum regularly though. She comes over to our place and helps me with the garden or with small decorating jobs within the house. Or I would go over with our little Susan, who we fondly started calling Sue. Dad loves to bounce her on his knee and let her fly like an aeroplane through the house.

Due to our tight financial situation, having to pay off the three parts of our home, the re-building and the new furniture, we decide not to have children any more.

For the first few years, I stayed at home to look after our little girl and to take care of the house and garden. Whenever possible, I would take on some needlework. My work is a welcome change, and helps us out a little on the financial side. Once Sue started primary school, I got my part-time job back as a cleaning help at the local school over the road from our cottage. This second stable income helped our situation a lot, and we soon became more flexible again. Nevertheless, we had been brought up in hard times. It's part of our flesh and blood to be careful with money, and to never be wasteful with anything. Bill and I are also more homely people. We are so proud of having a cottage of our own. We feel so comfortable at home that we have no desire to go out. The sunlight of our life is our little girl, Sue. Watching her grow-up is the greatest pleasure of all. Not only is she a beautiful blonde angel, but she also does very well at school and surprises us again and again with the best results in class.

She has made a best friend at school who is also called Sue and has the same blonde curls. It's funny watching the two blonde Sues play. They look like twins. At school, the children have started calling our Sue "CookE". So the children knock at our door and ask if "CookE" will come out and play. All my explanations that she is called Sue don't help. The name is starting to stick.

CHAPTER TEN

Sue's childhood was very sheltered and were the most peaceful years of our life. The world was blooming. Everything was going upwards. Great Britain has a new queen and a band called the Beatles is making young girls go crazy. In Church Stretton though, time stands still. If you don't want to, you don't need to know too much about what is going on in the world.

The three of us are doing well. Our little girl has grown up quite a bit, she and I love to spend time together sewing the latest fashions. Sue loves the short little dresses of the 60's. On Saturdays, we go for outings in the nearby town, Shrewsbury, and hunt for the newest fabrics. At home, we spend hours copying the latest fashions out of magazines. She looks lovely in the dresses, with her petite figure and long legs. I just wish the dresses were a little longer. But she will not hear about it, so I let her do her thing. She'll soon be off to university, which worries me a little. Especially hearing about all the raving parties going on in the world, and knowing the length of her skirts.

One morning, two letters arrive for Sue. They are from the Oxford and Sussex Universities. Sue will not be home until the afternoon, and Bill is at work. I'm standing alone in the kitchen. My excitement is overwhelming. Has she won entry to one of these universities? I have already held the letters towards the light, but cannot make out any words. I even thought of holding the envelopes over boiling water. This way the steam would probably melt the envelope's glue. I could have a peep and then seal them again without anybody noticing. My thoughts disgust me. The letters are not addressed to me. I will just have to wait.

I decide to occupy myself in the garden. Our garden is my pride, and offers plenty to do. Combining the once-three gardens together has made quite a large space. Our garden area is probably bigger than the whole ground that our house occupies. We have a greenhouse, a garden shed and a sheltered car park and washing line area. Most of the garden is bursting with plants. I just keep on seeing beautiful flowers that I cannot resist. And I won't let any of the existing plants go. Sometimes I drive Bill crazy. Wandering through the garden I talk to them and, if one looks a little out of place, I pep it up in our glass extension until it's okay to go out again. So it goes on, and my garden fills more and more. Some people even say it's more a jungle than a garden. I have left a little green space though. Next to the garden shed there is a little green patch with a heavy, cast-iron garden bench. On the other side of the grass, closer to the house, Bill has installed a birdhouse on stilts. From the kitchen window I have perfect view of what the birds are up to.

At 4:30 p.m., I start checking my watch every other minute. Sue must be home soon. This will be such an exciting moment of her life. She has done extremely well and achieved A's in all subjects. Turning the letters one more time, I can only imagine positive news.

The front door opens. It feels like sunlight is rushing into the house. Our beautiful girl is home. Smiling all over her face, she skips in through the front door and drops her bag near the staircase. I quickly bounce away from the kitchen counter, and pretend to just have cleared away some plates in the dresser. "Mum! Mum! Are you there? I'm home!" she cheerfully shouts from the landing. It doesn't take a second and she is standing in the living room, skips over and kisses me on the cheek. "Hey my love, you're home! How was your day?" I ask her, while giving her a quick squeeze. "Oh Mum, today was sports. I don't like it. But we were lucky, and Mrs Jones decided on tennis. So the girls and me had a lot of time to chat while we waited our turn. Do we have some biscuits? I'm starving!" She wanders over to the kitchen and vanishes into the pantry, totally ignoring the letters lying on the counter. From the pantry, I can hear paper wrappings rip and crinkle. "Mmmh, my favourite with the strawberry filling," I hear from the back. My daughter comes back with a biscuit in her hand and one obviously already in her mouth. She stops and leans against the kitchen counter. Slowly enjoying her biscuit, she scans the surface. "What's that?" she mumbles with full mouth. "There are two letters for you. From two universities," I beam at her. Her eyes widen with excitement. "Mum, why didn't you tell me?" She spurts and a piece of strawberry biscuit comes my way. Snatching the letter, she immediately rips them open.

The first one is from Oxford University. "Oh Mum, they are offering me a place with a full scholarship!" she screams, waving the letter above her head. Dancing from one foot to the other, she passes me the letter. With shaking hands I hold up the letter. Oxford! Oxford University wants our daughter and will take over all the fees and costs. This is unbelievable! My eyes water. I'm so proud!

While I am still trying to believe what I see in front of me, Sue is already opening the second letter. "Aaahhh, Mum, Sussex! I'm going to Sussex! Sussex is also offering me a full scholarship! Mum, Mum, Oh I was so much hoping they would take me!" Her eyes are wide with excitement. Cuddling the letter close to her heart, she elegantly spins around like a princess at her first ball. Seeing her like this makes my whole body tingle with happiness. Tears of joy for her young luck and tears of pride run down my face. I run over and hold her tight. Gently we swirl through the room.

Oxford is tempting. But maybe a little too stuffy for country people like us. We all agree. Sussex sounds more relaxed, and makes Sue shine all over her face. It's the place to be. It's down south, a relaxed atmosphere and a lot of exciting people to meet. Bill and I are not sure if we like that part. The security aspect would speak more for Oxford. But we don't really have a choice. Our girl has made her decision. Sussex University it will be.

While Sue cannot wait for the summer to end, it doesn't last long enough for Bill and I. Our girl is leaving! We have sat together and sewed some lovely dresses for her to take to university. Whenever I tried to cheat a few extra inches into the length, she, of course, caught me. An account with some money is ready for her at the bank. She has been able to get a room in the girl's Palace Pier accommodation. The pictures we have received look very promising, and it calms us to know that she has a safe home.

At the end of the summer, we drive Sue down to Brighton. The seaside town is bustling, with tourists enjoying the late summer sun on the beach. Down at the pier, there is a smell of sun cream lotion, toffee apples and popcorn. Happy music is playing from the beachside stalls. The atmosphere is carefree, young and happy. Getting closer to the university's dormitory area, the excitement in the air is touchable. Sue is sharing a lovely bright room with Anna. Anna is from up north. She's a bright girl with lovely long, dark brown hair. They will make good friends. Once all is settled and unpacked, it's time to say goodbye. It's the moment Bill and I have dreaded. It's the first time we will be separated from our daughter. "Mum, Dad, I will be home soon for a long weekend. Don't worry. I will be fine and we will telephone every weekend, I promise!" She tries to calm us, but I cannot stop my tears. "We will miss you so much, my love. It will be empty at home without you!" I sob. My heart feels like it's clamped between two bench vices. Slowly the bolts are tightened, making me gasp for air. The pressure builds and builds, and I feel that my heart will rip any moment. I swallow to try and release a little of the tension. Bill is standing next to me. He cannot say a word. He knows he will break if he does. He just reaches out, pulls Sue into his arms and holds her tight. "Dad, you're squashing me!" Sue protests with a laugh. Bill loosens his embrace and lays his large hands in a shielding way around her face and studies her features. "I will miss you my girl! Now, if you need anything, I mean anything at all, you know how to find us," he tells her in a serious way, and gently kisses her forehead before letting her go. Sue turns to me and takes my hands in hers. "Mum, are you okay?" she asks with a bright smile on her face and her eyes sparkling with excitement. "Oh, come here with you!" I order, and wrap her in my arms. "Look at me. I'm making a fool of myself," I can't control my tears anymore. They just roll down my face. "My little girl is at university. We are so proud of you! It's just all gone so quickly and we will miss you terribly," I sob, trying to catch my tears by dabbing my eyes with a handkerchief.

Slowly, Sue loosens herself from my grip. The three of us stand close together and she takes our hands. "Mum, Dad, thank you so much for making this possible for me. I love you so much and don't worry. I will be fine. All of this will be great for me. It's so exciting! But I will miss you too and I'll be home soon, remember!" She grabs us both at the same time, wraps her arms around our necks and pulls us close for a moment. Releasing us, she first kisses Bill and then me on the cheek. Then she turns, walks a few steps towards her room, turns one more time and waves. She looks so beautiful. Her long, silky hair is smoothly flowing down her back. Her eyes are as bright as two stars, excitedly taking in every detail. She is full of joy, ready for the long-awaited new chapter to begin. Her face is beaming and her whole appearance is bright and strong. Even though her build is fragile, she looks fairylike in one of her new dresses that show off her long skinny legs and sandals.

We both wave back. Then she turns and vanishes in her room. The two of us just stand and look at the now empty spot. We must look a little lost. I feel Bill's hand take mine and gently squeeze it. "Don't worry, Mollie. She will be fine!" He whispers to me and kisses my cheek. I sigh and we turn and slowly walk out of the building.

Outside, the sun is setting. Young people are sitting on the cobbled beach watching the goings-on. The atmosphere is calm and relaxed. The air tastes salty, and a cool breeze is growing. Above our heads, seagulls are busily flying up and down, taking sharp turns while releasing high-pitched shouts at each other. We drive home in silence. Both of us are caught-up in our thoughts. Trying to sort out our feelings.

Our little cottage has become quieter. It's just the two of us. Having more time, I have taken over some activities at the parish church. I enjoy being able to help and meet the locals. To some extent it fills the gap that Sue has left, and I don't sit around waiting to hear from our only child. At weekends, Bill and I enjoy strolling through our village or going to town. Collecting has always been a passion of mine. I love to spend time at antique markets and charity shops. Beautiful china, brass, colourful fabrics, lace and pretty bits and bobs are always ending up in my shopping bag. Our cottage is filling week by week. I am always finding a new little spot somewhere in one of our rooms that is in need of a piece.

My mother's health has suddenly started worsening, and I spend time with her whenever I can. We just sit and chat, or I help her with a bath and doing her hair. It's strange how our roles have suddenly changed. For as long as I can think, my mother was there for me. Standing by my side, holding me when I tripped. Washing my hair in our old bathtub in the kitchen and cleaning my clothes. Supporting me with advice and drying my tears. She was always a proud and strong lady. Making sure we didn't miss anything. Working hard while our Dad was far away at war. Filling the gap he left, and finding ways so that we would not suffer when goods were scarce.

My father calls me on an autumn Sunday afternoon. His voice is low and quiet. It sounds like the line is bad. But it's not. It's his deep sadness and fear that is breaking up the lines as he tries to speak. "Mollie, my dear, it's me, Dad. Uum, the doctors have just been here," his voice drops. "Mum has fallen asleep," he swallows. "She will not wake up again. She has gone and left us." His last words are only a fraction. I can hear his tears falling while he tries to catch his breath. But further words fail to come out. I swallow hard.

We knew this day was coming, but I always ignored the fact that her sickness had weakened her so much. I kept it far away from me, so I wouldn't have to think about it. It was all easier that way.

"Oh Dad, I'm so sorry!" I grasp the chest of drawers on which our telephone is standing. The cool wood beneath my hand feels smooth and clean. Holding on to the chest helps me keep my balance. "Are you okay, Dad?" I can hear my father swallow on the other end of the line. "Bill and I will be over in half an hour. Don't worry. We will be there soon!" I reassure him. "Okay my dear, I better call the boys. See you in a bit." The line goes dead, and there is only the dialling tone.

I stand with the receiver still to my ear, and just stare out of the small window next to the chest of drawers. I don't actively see anything. I am just staring into the air.

In the other room, I can hear Bill in the kitchen. His steps are coming closer. "Mollie! Everything okay?" He asks, opening the door to the landing. I place the receiver down and look at him blankly. "Dear? What has happened?" He walks over and takes me into his arms. "Mum has left us. She died this morning." A wave of emotions hits me as I realise my own words. My eyes cloud up with tears. "Dad just called." My voice breaks and tears spill down my cheeks. Bill presses me hard to his warm body. "I am so sorry, Mollie. I know how much she meant to you," he says as he gently strokes my back.

A survival mode suddenly takes over me. I wipe away my tears with the back of my hand. I look up into Bill's calm, deep-green eyes. It's as if I can see deep into his soul. He lets me do this. He wants me to know that he will always be by my side, to protect and support me. Always full of love, trust and honesty towards me, without taking any space, only giving. All of this and much more is what I find within him. His security strengthens me. Gently, he strokes away the drying remnants of my tears while watching me. "I will get the car keys. Your Dad needs us!" he says with a warm smile.

The week leading up to my mothers' funeral went by in a flash. My survival mode allowed me to organize everything quickly, giving my father space to grieve. The ceremony was simple and followed the ritual of the church. I don't like to make up any special things for events like this. I feel that a classic ceremony is the right thing to do. Let a loved-one go in a simple and easy way, without making too much pomp and splendour. Bill and I have offered to let my Dad spend some time at our home. He doesn't want to, though. He prefers to stay at his home in Cunnery Road. In this case, I have to say I am glad he is an outgoing type. He enjoys meeting people, going down to the pub for a chat or a game of dominoes. In company of his friends, he feels supported and at home.

Weeks after the funeral, my survival modes switches off and reality hits me. My dear mother is gone. I catch myself talking to her as if she was still here. I don't think this is a bad thing to do. I believe messages are always received in one or the other way. But it makes me realise how much I miss her. How large the gap is that she has left. How much I miss spending time with her. Telling her all my stories. Sharing experiences and talking through the tactics that are needed for this and that. Through my work at the local school and my activities for the parish church, I do have regular contact with locals. Bill and I have kept quite to ourselves though. I have some friends with whom I sometimes do some shopping and have a cup of tea down the village. But I don't otherwise really share too much with other people. It's all been quite internal. Bill and me, Sue and me and my mother and me.

Wrapped in a thick cardigan I sit outside in our garden. Autumn is already nearly ending. There are not many colourful leaves left on our plants. Most of them have already fallen to the ground. They have turned to a dark, soggy-looking brown on the damp earth. A fine layer of mist is hovering over the dark brown soil. Above the smoke-like mist, bare stems are stretching themselves for a last time towards the dull looking sky. It looks like they are screaming for a last ray of warm sunlight before collapsing to the ground. It's not an inspiring day. It's a day that reminds me of everything we still need to do before the snow arrives.

Emptiness widens inside me. I suddenly feel very much alone. Nothing going upwards or left to do. Only the tasks of closing down for the coming winter are in front of me. I feel bizarre, as tears of sadness shoot into my eyes and roll down my cheek. But, inside, I know it's not the garden that is upsetting me. It's the loss of my mother, my close friend and companion that is hitting me.

Spontaneously, I decide to leave the garden. I need space and different surrounding. Leaving our cottage, I walk up the lane to the country fence that leads up the hill to the wood. The walk up the steps takes my breath away. Arriving at the top of the grassy green slope, I sit down on the old wooden bench. In front of me, Church Stretton and the neighbouring hills stretch out. Smoke from chimneys slowly makes its way up into the sky. It's a grey day. The village seems calm and quiet. Two magpies sitting on a branch are shouting at each other. One of the birds notices me, and starts carefully study-ing me with his black, pin-type eyes. It doesn't even seem to notice or mind that his companion has spread his wings and left the scene. Quietly, we both sit and watch each other. Now and then, the magpie moves his head from one side to the other in a robotic style. Suddenly, the bird squeals at me in an asking way. It feels like the bird is telling me off or accusing me of something. Sitting on the bench wrapped in my warm cardigan, I feel like a child being told off for doing something bad. "Okay, okay. You can stop now!" I shake my head - I'm talking to a magpie.

The bird clumsily walks along the branch, always keeping me in his sight. I wish I had his wings and could fly. I would fly away and leave this damp and chilly place. Go somewhere dryer and warm. Somewhere more colourful with pretty flowers. The magpie turns its head and puffs his feathers. Within seconds, it looks like his body has doubled in size. A large dropping falls to the ground with a thud, sticking on the green grass. "Charming" I call out. The magpie turns its head and looks me in the eye. "Well, now I know why you were shouting at me. You obviously needed a moment for yourself." The scene with the magpie and me makes me grin. How peculiar is this? I shake my head and feel my spirits lift. Getting to my feet, I decide to stroll through the forest for a while and collect some sticks. Concentrating on little things will give my mind a rest. And we always can do with some wood for the Rayburn.

CHAPTER ELEVEN

It's very exciting. Our little Sue has met someone at university whom she really likes. She is over the moon, and they are coming to visit us for a weekend. It seems serious. Well, that's what I think after hearing my daughter going on about it forever on the phone. But Bill wouldn't put it that way. His little girl is serious with some city boy? No way! She is much too young. She would probably have to be 40-plus to be allowed to be serious with someone if it was up to Bill. While tidying up our living room, I smirk at my thoughts. Dads and their baby girls. They are so protective. Well, in our case, I guess it's a bit over the top, as we only have one child. I'm happy for Sue that she has got to know someone nice. I wouldn't want her to start a family as late as I did. It will be nice if she can have a family at a young age. She will have time, and could have more than one child. We have space for some more family members. The thought of being a Nana fills me with pride. But what am I thinking of? Gosh, she's just introducing us to her boyfriend and I am already thinking of my grandchildren. Shaking my head at my own thoughts, I go on dusting all the accessible surfaces. Yes, it has become kind of crowded in our cottage. But there are still some spaces for which I'm sure to find the one or the other nice piece to stand on, sooner or later. Maybe I will just pop down the village later on for a browse. We will anyway need some additional groceries for the weekend.

Down the village, I visit the antique market. The Church Stretton antique market is a permanent market in an old building on the High Street. Old furniture, antiques and a lot of rubbish are displayed on four floors. The top two floors are mainly filled with furniture. I don't tend to visit these areas very often. I prefer the lower floors. These are filled with china, brass, books, wicker baskets, jewellery, tools and lot more odd bits and bobs. Exactly my kind of things.

On a large wooden table filled with all sorts of china, I spot a beautiful teapot. It's made of white china and has pretty purple flowers painted all over it. The lovely curved handle has a crack up the side. Carefully I turn the pot in hope to find the price on its bottom. And there it is. A white sticker is stuck to the bottom of the pot. With a thick black pen, five pounds has been written on it. Hmm, that's not bad. The cracked handle must be the reason for the reduced price, I think. The crack doesn't disturb me. I think it tells a story and makes the item one of a kind. I wonder what happened. Did it fall to the ground during a tea party? Was it unknowingly bumped by other jugs and plates in an over-full cupboard? Did it get into a child's unskilled fingers? Or was it removal damage? Maybe the teapot was traveling to or from faraway places? Turning the teapot back around, I eye it up again. I like the dainty flowers. They are painted in my favourite colour, lilac. The spout of the pot has an elegant curve, and the top opening is large. Large enough to use the pot as a new home for some pretty flowers. It will look lovely in our living room window.

Proudly clutching my newly-found treasure, I walk to the cashier. All I will need now are some pretty flowers. Next, I will go to the small gardening centre across the road.

Late Friday afternoon, Sue and her new boyfriend arrive at our house. The two of them are grinning goofy smiles all over their faces and nervously squeezing each other's hand. Most shocking though is that our princess has cut off her lovely hair. She is standing in front of us with a short pixie haircut. Her colourful dress is just as short. Did I help her making that, I ask myself. Her boyfriend, Chris, is from up north. He is a Manchester boy. He is wearing tight trousers and a white shirt that shows off his too slim build. His thick jet-black hair is the darkest I've ever seen. It's very unique, a little too long and combed to one side. Quite peculiar is that his moustache has a reddish touch. There must be some copper in his family tree.

The four of us enjoy dinner together. The two young ones tell us all about their exciting university life on campus. The fancy dress parties they have, and how music has become an important part of their life. The content of their discussions are different to the ones we used to have. But the situation reminds me of Bill and me with my parents, sitting at the dinner table talking for hours. Hasn't time flown! Now here we are with our child. Generations have come and gone. What has happened to all the years? Have we grown old without noticing? No, we're not old! We're not even grandparents yet. I calm myself. There is still a lot to come. A lot of new heart-filling and tear-shedding experiences are still to be made.

The weekend goes by in a flash. Bill and I can hardly keep up with the speed of our soon-to-be tweens. They are full of beans. Always doing something or going somewhere.

On Sunday afternoon. It's already time to say goodbye. We give them a lift down to the station. Both of them stand in front of us, beaming all over their faces. Chris goes and organises the train tickets, which gives us some time with our daughter.

"Mum, Dad, what do you think?" she asks us all smiley, jumping from one leg to the other. "He seems very nice. Has a lot to say and knows everything. Very bright!" I reply. "Most important of all, is that he takes care of you, dear. And is a good companion. Someone you can totally rely on and who is your best friend. If you both achieve that, it doesn't matter what happens. You will always be happy together," I add, and stroke the side of her face with my hand. Bill seems lost for words. I know it must hurt him to have to share his only girl. Sue pins him with her gaze. "Come here my girl," he orders. He holds out his strong arms to cuddle her. No more words are needed. Together they stand and embrace each other, and she rests her head on his chest. "I love you Dad!" She whispers. Bill closes his eyes and kisses her short hair. "Now, if you need anything, you know how to reach us," he tells her, loosening his grip.

Chris is back with two train tickets in his hand. A little lost, he stands next to us. Sue's eyes are sparkling with youthful love as she sees him. Quickly she kisses her Dad's cheeks before bouncing over to me. "Mum, see you soon. And don't buy too many teapots," she smiles, with a wicked look on her face. Flinging her arms around my neck, she hugs me hard and kisses my cheeks. A second later, she's standing next to Chris and her hand is finding his. The two of them pick up their weekender, smile at us with glowing eyes, turn and walk to their train.

Bill and I are left alone on the platform. My eyes are still stuck to the spot where my daughter stood a few seconds ago. My thoughts are spinning. They cannot keep up. Was I not just giving birth to my daughter? Helping her making her first steps? Playing in the garden together? Sitting next to her while she did her homework? And now? She is all grown up. Doing her thing. At university, meeting new friends and finding her matching piece. I sigh, and feel Bills fingers wrapping around mine. He presses my hand with his. Looking up at him, I see him smiling down at me. His eyes are calm and warm. But, somehow, a wave of pain is mixed in. We smile at each other. Bill bends down and kisses me. "My lady, shall we go home?" He asks me. I wink at him and together we turn and walk back to our car. Our hands never loosen or leave each other. The warmth, the place of home and the feeling of protection are needed too much. It's just him and me now. And we are happy.

CHAPTER TWELVE

Bill and I are upstairs in our bedroom. A sense of excitement and happiness lies in the air. Nervously, Bill tries to get his tie straight. He's not doing very well. His fingers are all shivery, and any minute he will get all worked up about it. I can sense this. I step in before a mini-explosion of nerves occurs. "Let me help you!" I hold both of his shaking hands in mine. "I'm not used to these things anymore," he complains and smiles at me relieved. "Sit down on the bed. We don't want me to get a stiff neck now, do we? How would that look if I am at the registrar's office looking like this?" Playing the fool, I dance around the bed with my head stretched-up towards the ceiling in a sideward way. My eyes wide open and my lips stretched to a thin line across my face. Showing off a little of my teeth. "Okay, okay, I am sitting down, Mrs Shorty-legs," Bill surrenders with a roar of laughter and flops on the bed. "You know that one day that will stick!" he warns me. "Well, that's the advantage of being married. You don't need to be out impressing the other sex. I have you and you have me. We are settled, never mind what happens," I tease, and start straightening the tie around his neck.

"There you go, wonderful!" I step back and admire my husband. He looks lovely! He is wearing a dark brown suit with matching tie and a crisp white shirt. A pink flower is fastened to the top buttonhole of his jacket. His fair hair is neatly combed back, showing off his happy face. I love Bill's face. It's such a beautiful happy face. His green eyes are always sparkling and smiley. His features are calm and down to earth. Somebody you immediately feel comfortable with.

I myself am wearing a two-piece suit. A 'deux-piece' as the French would call it. It's a lovely powder blue, with matching hat and shiny beige shoes with a little heel. Looking in the mirror, I admire the fact that my new shoes make me a little taller. I like that.

"We'd better be on our way, dear," I hear Bill shout. He's down in the kitchen. "We don't want to be late for our only child's wedding!" he adds. "No, we don't," I say to myself. "I'm coming!" I grab my handbag and make my way down the stairs.

We don't say too much sitting in the car. We're both caught in our thoughts. Our girl is getting married. She is only 21 years old. A little early to get married, we both think. But she is so happy and in love. Since meeting Chris, she always has been very determined that he will be the one she will marry. At first we thought it was just a phase. She would meet others on campus and change her mind over and over again. But she didn't. She knew what she wanted, and she was going to have it. She always did. That's our Sue.

The two of them have stayed down south after university. They don't have much money, but they are happy. And today is their day. They are getting married. The ceremony will take place at the registrar's office. Nothing too fancy, just a regular ceremony followed by a lovely dinner. Getting married so quickly after university didn't give them any time to save some money for a larger wedding. But even if they had had the time, they probably wouldn't have used their money for that. Sue is already looking forward too much to a house with garden of her own. She also wants a family. She loves children and can't wait to have a few of her own.

The wedding ceremony is simple, and held in a modern office. The bride and groom's excitement and their love for each other are so overwhelming that the surroundings just fade away. It's a joy to watch them. So young and so full of love. It warms my heart and fills me with hope for her future. Our girl will be happy. That I can see in front of me, and feel it deep down inside.

Chris is dressed in a dark suit and fresh white shirt. He also has a pink flower attached to the top buttonhole of his jacket. His long black hair is combed to one side as usual. Sue is wearing a green velvet, two-piece suit. Her skirt is very short. I was hoping she would go for something longer on her wedding day. But it's just not what the young people wear nowadays. The 60's have been all about short dresses and the Beatles. I am in hope that the coming 70's will be calmer again. On the front collar of her jacket, she has attached a beautiful brooch that I have given her for the university degree. The white ivory colour matches wonderfully to the green colour of her suit.

In the registrar's office, Bill and I sit in comfortable padded chairs to one side of the room. On the other side, in identical chairs, Chris's family members are seated. In front of us, our two children are nervously shuffling around on their chairs while holding each other's hand. We don't really know Chris' family. His Mum and Dad, the two brothers and both aunts on his Mum's side have come to the ceremony. His mother, Edith, is dressed in an elegant, silvery grey coloured dress, which is topped by a dark, broad-brimmed hat. Her hair is the same dark, black colour as Chris. It shows off her porcelain skin, which looks soft, like a thin layer of silk that covers her fine features. She is a city girl who must have come from a good family. We learned from Chris that she fell in love during the Second World War with Albert, a sailor in the Royal Navy and got married quite quickly. He now works as a salesman and is driving all over the country. With three boys, money is quite tight and Chris had to fight his way through university.

Edith has a very close relationship with her sisters. That is immediately noticeable. They even look almost identical. All three of them with the same dark hair and facial features. All dressed very elegantly in the latest city fashion. They are a little intimidating.

Chris's brothers are younger than he is. They don't seem to be bothered about what is going on. I would even go so far to say they look a little bored. But I guess as teenagers you would prefer other activities than sitting in a registrar's office for a wedding ceremony, even if it's your brother's wedding.

Albert, Chris' Dad, is a tall, slim man with silvery-grey hair. You can tell that he must have been a good-looking young man who easily won girls' hearts. He looks tired though, and a little worn out. I assume this comes from his job, driving for hours every day. Enduring the constant pressure of having to sell in order to be able to feed his family.

He is surrounded by a light smell of tobacco. It's easy to see that he smokes cigarettes without actually smelling the smoke. His index and middle finger on his right hand have a yellow stain on the inside. He seems a little uneasy. I'm sure that it has to do with the situation, though I don't think it has to do with us. He doesn't seem like a person who has problems meeting other people. Standing there not knowing what to say doesn't seem to be his thing. Actually, he is probably the one who is normally the centre of attention. The wrinkles around the corners of his lips give away that he is a smiley, fun person. Somebody who often enjoys a good laugh and loves to have a little fun with you. I think this uneasiness goes back to his smoking habit. Sitting there, knowing he possibly will not have the chance to smoke for a while. Thinking of the possible opportunities to escape, and coming to the conclusion that none will really work, or would only make him look silly. And then, only a split second after his thoughts, telling himself off for even thinking of something like that at his eldest son's wedding.

Breathing in deeply and slowly exhaling I lean back against my chair and relax my shoulders. My girl is in front of me. Her short hair has a light curl and makes her neck look long and elegant. She is whispering something to Chris. Her eyes are bright and sparkling, and her smile covers her whole face. The registrar clears his throat and the room quietens down. All eyes are fixed to the front. The ceremony begins.

After a lot of talk about love, caring for each other and marriage, the rings are exchanged. They have chosen thick silver wedding bands. Nervously, but full of joy, they stand and look each other in the eye while speaking their wedding vows, first Chris, followed by Sue. Seeing her slipping the wedding ring on his finger makes tears shoot into my eyes. I cannot stop them. They are too many and too fast. Some are tears of happiness for my daughter. Pride of what she has achieved in her short life. Knowing she has her whole life in front of her. A career, children of her own and travelling the world. Everything is possible. All doors are open. Which will she choose? Through which will she really walk? Will she find true happiness? Some other tears are for myself. Tears for losing my only child, and tears remembering my past. My first wedding with Jack, then Bill and myself. The overwhelming happiness and gratefulness I felt. I was blessed to have found a true and deep love a second time in one lifetime.

I have never forgotten Jack. He was my first true love. A man I had so much hope in. I dreamt of him every night. I would write to him every day and tell him about my thoughts and feelings. I spoke my vows in front of church and our families, and promised to always be his. What happened to this promise? Was it all just a pink castle in the clouds? Did I do wrong? But what was I supposed to do? Live with my parents to the end of my life? Alone, without anybody to hold me at night? These are my own dark thoughts and worries. I don't speak them out, or share them with anyone. I used to do this with my mother, but she was the only one. Now I share them with her in my thoughts, hope they reach her and that she answers me.

Luckily, I knew this would happen, and I am well prepared with a pretty hanky in my jacket pocket. Dabbing my eyes, I catch Bill in the corner of my eye. He is not so well prepared, and is trying to casually dry his tears with his index finger and the back of his hand. An overwhelming rush of love towards him overcomes me. I must have done something right to have deserved such a sensitive and loving man! Gently I nudge him with my right arm. Caught in the action, he shyly smiles over to me. His eyes are still watery. But this is allowed at weddings.

"You may kiss the bride," the registrar announces. Both fall into each other's embrace in front of us, and happily kiss. My daughter is now officially called Susan Mary Lee.

CHAPTER THIRTEEN

Sue looks like she will burst or fall over frontwards any minute. Our daughter has a very slim figure. She always had. If she didn't make her own clothes, she would have to look in the children's' department for something pretty that would fit her. She is so petite. Looking at her, pregnant at last, I always wonder how she keeps her balance. Her tummy has gone enormous.

She has had to be patient. It took her four years to become pregnant. We have had numerous calls or talks in the garden together. It has been frustrating for her, and she couldn't understand why it took so much time. Every month waiting to see if her cycle has changed. Ending in frustration, and then building new hope for the next month. I have understood and felt every word she said. But I was also pleased that she and Chris had a little time for just the two of them. To enjoy their time together after university. Making their first experiences at work and earning some money, without the pressure of having to feed a family. Everything has its purpose. Her angel took its time to choose her. I think that's a good sign.

She has been so proud of herself over the last nine months. She has loved her bump and happily showed it off.

Her cheeks have filled, and she looks all happy and full of sunshine. Her regrown hair surrounds her face like a waterfall. Nothing can disturb her. She is constantly stroking her belly and secretly talking to her little one. Her love to her unborn child is overwhelming, and is pouring out of every pore.

Bill and I are very excited that we will soon have a new family member. We can't wait to hear little feet tapping across the floor, calling out our new names, Granddad and Nana. And we are happy to know that the Cooke's genes will live on, even with another name.

Our phone rings early in the morning. It's a very cold Sunday. Being more asleep than awake at this early hour, neither Bill nor I feel like jumping out of the warm bed. After the second demanding ring, we awake properly. Bill jumps out of bed, slips on his slippers and dressing gown, and rushes downstairs to answer the phone. Rubbing my eyes, I sit up and lean against the cool wall. It's still dark outside. I can tell that even though our curtains are drawn. There's no light shining through the dark fabric. The only light shining into our bedroom is coming from the landing. A bright yellow light-path has made its way across our bedroom carpet, showing up every single crumb of dust. "I must hoover," I think to myself in dismay at the sight. Downstairs, I can hear Bill take the call with a croaky voice. "Bill Cooke! Oh Chris, hi," his voice dies down. "Oh, okay. I understand. Don't worry, all will go well. We will be on our way. See you soon! Yes. Yes, take care of our girl! Okay, bye for now." The receiver bumps down. "Mollie! Time to get dressed. Sue is in labour. I'll make us some tea," Bill excitedly shouts up. "Sue is in labour?" I shout out of the bed. "Yes. Chris has driven her to the hospital. They think it will take some time. But it will take us a while to drive down south. So we'd better get going!" Electrified, I jump out of bed. For a second, my eyes cloud up and all goes black in front of me. I lean against our bed and wait for the moment to pass. Our bedroom comes back into sight. I quickly walk into the bathroom to wash myself. Ah, our grandchild is coming! I think to myself. It's coming!

The cold water that I splash into my face wakens me. I quickly slip on a tartan skirt and matching jumper. "That will do. I already look kind of Nana-style," I smirk to myself in the mirror. Bill appears in the bedroom with a cup of hot black tea. "Here you go, love." He places the mug down on the dresser and turns for the bathroom without waiting for any response. Calm Bill is excited too.

15 minutes later we are sitting in our small car. Bill steers down the lane and onto the main road. I wish I could press the accelerator with my foot and speed things up.

We arrive at the hospital towards lunchtime. The receptionist takes all the time in the world to look up the room that Sue has been brought to. Once we are in the right wing, we try to settle down in the waiting room. Chris soon joins us. He has got quite some colour in his face. His eyes look tired and worried though. "She has been in labour for 12 hours now," he explains. "It's all very slow. But we are now getting close. I need to get back. I just wanted to update you." He quickly hugs both of us and rushes out again. Bill and I are left in the sparse waiting room. A young nurse appears at the door, dressed all in white. "Can I fetch you a cup of tea?" she kindly asks us. "That would be lovely! Thank you!" I return. She smiles at us before leaving. "Well, I guess we just need to wait and make the best out of it!" Bill explains, and gestures to a chair. The two of us sit down. It's not really comfortable though. The chairs are hard and have no padding. I anxiously play with my wedding ring. "Don't worry Mollie. Our girl is a tough cookie. She'll be okay!" he calms me. The nurse appears back with two cheap cups of black tea. We don't mind though. The warm fluid feels good after the long drive.

About 30 minutes later, Chris is back with us in the waiting room. "Mollie, Bill, he's here! Matthew has arrived. He's wonderful. A beautiful boy! You can come and see him," Chris is totally excited, and his cheeks have reddened. Bill and I just stand there with open mouths. "A boy!" shoots through my head. "Matthew, Matthew," I repeat the name in my mind.

"It's been difficult though," Chris carries on. "They had to make a cut to help the baby out. Sue has lost a lot of blood and is very weak," he explains. "They even sent me out of the room because they thought it would be too much for me. This upset Sue and myself a lot," he complains. "I did want to be there," he grumbles. This is all quite modern for Bill and I. Nowadays, fathers are with their wives at birth. That didn't used to be the case in our time. It was normal that the men stayed out, and waited till the baby cried out loud. "Well, are you ready to meet your grandson?" Chris beams at us. "What are we waiting for? We can't wait!" I smile back at him, and clutch Bills hand tightly.

We follow Chris down the grey corridor. The smell of antiseptic tickles my nose. I don't like hospitals. I don't like check-ups and people that I don't know in white clothing touching me. There are too many illnesses in hospitals. Who knows what you will pick-up and leave with.

At Room 235, Chris turns to us. "Here we go," he smiles and opens the door. A dull room opens up in front of us. All is white and grey. In the middle of the room, a single bed is standing with its headpiece against the wall. Our daughter is lying in the bed with her eyes closed. She looks tired and worn. There is a pool of thick red blood underneath the bed. It's the only real colour in the room. The picture looks strange from a distance. Bill and I just stand there in shock. "They haven't cleaned up yet," Chris explains. "The blood is from the cut. I don't know what they are messing at."

Chris's voice wakens Sue. She opens her eyes, looks over and smiles at us. Her whole face lights up with pride and makes me forget the surroundings. She has waited so many years for this day. And now it is here. She's a mother! "Mum, Dad, why are you standing there? Come over! The nurses should be back soon with Matthew. He is being cleaned-up. He wants to make a good impression," she giggles, with a wicked look in her eye.

We sit around her bed and I hold her hand. "Oh, he is such a lovely boy, Mum! You have to see him. He is gorgeous! He didn't cry a second." Sue is over the moon. "But how are you, my love? You look very tired. Are you in pain?" I cannot hide my worries. My daughter looks very weakened, and from where I am sitting I can just see a corner of the pool of red blood that is slowly drying and turning to a brownish colour. Sue looks at me with tired but sparkly eyes. "Don't worry, Mum! I only need a little sleep and I will be fine. It looks worse than it is. I mean, it wasn't easy, but now he's here, and healthy. That's all that matters."

A knock at the door interrupts us. Carefully, the door opens and a nurse with a white bundle on her arm walks into the room. "Here you go, Sue. Little Matthew has had his first bath and is ready to meet the family," she smiles, and hands over the little bundle to Sue. "Now, if you need anything, just ring this bell," she gestures to a red button that is hanging down on a cord at the top end of the bed. "Oh dear, they haven't cleaned up this here yet, have they." The nurse inspects the pool of blood at the bottom of the bed. Her left eyebrow arches and a deep breath underlines her displeased expression. With her hands on her hips, she marches out of the room. "I will send someone in to sort that out," she pronounces in a business-like manner, and closes the door.

Here he is. Little Matthew is comfortably resting in a soft white towel on Sue's arm. His blurry eyes are staring up to the ceiling. He's a wonderful sight. My heart feels so touched that it hurts. For once, I seem incapable of saying a word. I just sit and stare at my grandson. The overwhelming love I feel growing strongly inside of me is unconditional. It doesn't matter what happens, I will always be there for him. I can feel the change happening inside of me. It's like my heart is growing. A new and deep piece is building with rapid speed, only for little Matthew. It's one of these rare moments in life when you know something has changed forever. It doesn't matter what happens. This new piece will always be with me. An expansion of myself, and not even death can take this part away. Looking at his little face reminds me of my feelings after giving birth to Sue. It felt the same, as if my heart was breaking. But it wasn't breaking. It was growing. Tears of happy pain run down my face. But I am not the only one. Looking across the bed, I see Bill. He is trying to control his watery eyes by heavily swallowing. His cheeks have gone all pink, and a glow of love and pride has surrounded him.

In the coming weeks, we spend a lot of time down south helping Sue and Chris with little Matthew. He is a wonderful baby boy. Bill and I cannot stop making pictures of him in every possible situation and showing them to everybody. We are so proud! I cannot wait to hear him call me "Nana" for the first time.

Time flies with a child. We are always doing something. Visiting our daughter or being visited by her. The times in-between we spend buying little bits and pieces for children and showing off our first grandson.

Matthew has started walking and is all over the place. He has grown beautiful, with angel-like white hair. Nobody can resist him. You can see him coming for miles. His beautiful hair bounces with every clumsy step he takes. His big blue eyes can charm a duck off a pond. He loves gardens. Being out sitting somewhere in the green and playing with sticks keeps him happy for ages. He is Bill's pride and joy. The two of them love to wander through our garden. It's a funny sight seeing them walk off, hand in hand. Bill is bent to one side to be able to hold his small hand.

Looking forward to seeing our grandchild grow-up made the quiet passing of my own father easier to handle. It wasn't sudden. My father, Jack, had reached a grand old age and I knew the moment of our goodbye was close. Being distracted by a wonderful new-born took my thoughts off it though. I was happy for my Dad that he could leave this world peacefully in his sleep. Reliving our shared memories at his funeral left me in tears for days and I bless little Matthew for filling a part of the empty space he has left. New memories will grow and feed my heart for the future.

My youngest brother's daughter, Barbara, came back to England to study some years ago. Fred and Joyce stayed in South Africa with their adopted son Glyn. Barbara got stuck in England and married George. Today, they have two sons of their own. Bill and I see Barbara and her family on a regular basis. They don't live too far away, and she has become one of our closest family contacts. For Barbara, I think we are a compensation for her parents, who are so far away. She is a lovely young mother, and I enjoy spending time with her, chatting about life. We plan to fly to South Africa together one day. Even though we enjoy talking about it, I know it is still far away for me. One day this trip will come. But it won't be soon.

It's a late autumn day on a lovely weekend. Sue, Chris and Matthew are visiting us.

Bill and Matthew are out in the garden, brushing up the colourful autumn leaves. Well, I don't know if you can really call it brushing up. Every time they have a pile of leaves together, Matthew pounces into them and throws them all over the place again with a loud squeal. Sue, Chris and I are sitting around the Rayburn having a cup of tea. "Mum, we are trying to get pregnant again," Sue beams at me. "Matthew needs a friend. It will be wonderful to see him with a little sister or brother. He won't ever be lonely and I would love to have another one," she explains. "We are hoping for a girl. It would be perfect to have one of each," Chris adds, taking Sue's hand. Both look so happy and in love. "That is wonderful. We were wondering what you are waiting for," I smile at them. Outside, we can hear Matthew squeal with laughter. Bill must be playing aeroplanes with him. It's a wonderful sound. "Well you know, Bill is going to retire next spring. So the timing is right. We will have much more time to help you look after Matthew. Bill will love it!" I giggle. The three of us sit together, and enjoy a moment of peace and let our thoughts drift off to baby number two.

And so it comes that, punctually with regard to Bill's retirement, Sue announces the good news. She is pregnant. Their second child is expected at the end of November. We can't wait for the winter to come.

Bill's retirement doesn't make a big change in our lives. Working close to our cottage always meant that he was home a lot. We were therefore used to being together all the time, and enjoyed this very much. He occasionally drives the hearse to funerals to earn a little extra now and then, even after he stopped work as a mechanic. We spend most of our days at home. We absolutely love our cottage and garden, and we feel comfortable being at home. Every other day, we walk down the village and buy our groceries or go for a walk up the hills and collect firewood for the Rayburn and wild blueberries for a dessert or jam. My obsession to collect pretty things is taking its toll, I must admit. Our cottage is getting quite full, even though there are only the two of us. Luckily, Bill has taken a liking to brass and has become quite a collector of horse brasses, which he proudly hangs around the Rayburn. This takes me a little out of the spotlight.

On November 21st, our family grows again. Little Kathy is born on a cold November night. Bill and I had only just arrived at their home when Chris had to rush off to hospital with Sue. Kathy was in a hurry to arrive. The birth only took a couple of hours. This time everything went easy and smooth. Maybe a little too smooth. Sue's first words were "I want to do this again," Chris told us, with a bit of a worried expression on his face.

A girl, a little sister for Matthew. She has no choice but to be his friend. He pounces on her whenever he can. He is a proud big brother now. His face shines whenever he is allowed to sit on the settee with her in his arms. Overnight, he has turned into a big boy, even though he is only a toddler. Kathy is soon quite a handful. She is always up to something. Her red curls and green eyes complement her mischievous plans. Having another girl in the family gets my hopes high to one day have a accomplice collector of pretty things. I can already see myself with her in town, looking at pretty fabrics for dresses, like I did with Sue. Growing up with two brothers made me used to being with boys and playing rough games. But I did enjoy time with my mother and, later on, doing girly things with my daughter. Having a grand-daughter completed the line.

But the family planning of my daughter was not finished. Kathy's birth was too nice an experience. And so it was that, three years later, David was born on a warm summer day. Rather different from Kathy though. David was in no hurry to come at all. Already beyond the calculated date of birth, little David took all time in the world to join us. He even fell asleep during the procedure, which meant waiting until he woke up again to carry on. He finally arrived though.

The way he joined us is the way he has stayed. A quiet child who loves his sleep. A dream for every parent - he is no problem at all. A special bond seemed to grow between him and Sue. Maybe it's because she knows that this is her last child, and she therefore needs to soak up every moment even more. Or maybe it's another sense that we cannot understand.

The three of them meant the world to Bill and me. Every one of them is so individual. But which grandparent wouldn't say that.

CHAPTER FOURTEEN

Bill and I are both nervously dashing back and forth from our bedroom to the small backroom where we have set up our suitcases. What to take? What's the weather like in Switzerland? Well, we'd better pack enough, I think to myself. We have only ever heard of Switzerland from magazines or the "Heidi" book. So what we know is that it is a beautiful mountain place. A lot of snow, wild flowers and peaceful lakes, that's the picture we have. We have never thought of actually going there. We have never travelled much. Bill and I are more homely type of people. Sometimes we would go to the Welsh coast or down south to visit family, but not much further. And now we are off for a two-week visit to our daughter and family in Switzerland.

The news of their move abroad hit us some months ago. Chris had been offered a two-year contract with a partner company in Switzerland. They quickly decided to take on the adventure. All their favourite furniture and clothes were packed and shipped to their new destination, a small city in Switzerland called Zug. They have rented out their house as they plan to be back in a couple of years. Now, a couple of months later, all has arrived and they have moved into a newly-built flat and are getting settled down. So it's a good time for us to visit.

The news of their leaving for Switzerland was quite a shock for both of us. It saddened me to think of my main family being so far away. There wouldn't be any weekend visits anymore. We will really miss seeing our grandchildren growing up. We will have to make the best out of summer holidays when they are back in England and the occasional visits of Bill and I to Switzerland.

"Mollie dear, how many trousers do you think I should take?" Bill is standing in front of our wardrobe. He is looking lost, staring at his clothes neatly hanging on wooden hangers on one side of our wardrobe. "Uh, I don't know. Sue said it was nice and warm. So I would go for the lighter ones. I think two or three should do. In the worst case, they do have washing machines over there. So you could get them washed if needed." I explain, standing next to him, and also staring into the dark wardrobe. "I will go with some of my pretty skirts." My face lightens up while I gently stroke the soft fabrics of my newly-made pieces. Bill nudges me with a smile and grabs three pairs of brown coloured trousers. "Right, now I need some matching shirts and I'm fine," he explains, laying out his choice on our bed. "What time is Morris picking us up tomorrow?" I ask, still gazing into the wardrobe. "He will be here at 8 a.m. That will give us enough time to find our way around the airport. And we will be in Switzerland by 3 p.m.," he smiles and his eyes dazzle. He misses his daughter very much. "Oh good! I don't like airports. Everyone is in such a rush and there are too many signs," I wrinkle my forehead at the thought.

We are up early the next day. Everything is settled. Our neighbour Nancy is taking care of our home. At exactly 8 a.m. there is a knock at our door. Morris is standing ready outside with his car. After making sure all the lights are off and all the doors are locked, our journey begins.

We arrive at the airport just before lunchtime. The check-in area is buzzing. There are people and suitcases everywhere. I'm glad we have enough time to figure this all out. All of this is just not our generation anymore. The assistant at the desk is very kind though, and helps us with all our questions. Our two suitcases are loaded onto a conveyer belt. I can't help wondering how they will make it to the right plane. They only have a small sticky ticket stuck to the handle. It all seems very cleverly done to me. I already feel exhausted after the security and passport control. We flop down on one of the comfortably padded chairs in a coffee area. A young waitress organizes us tea and a sandwich - I am starving. We have another 40 minutes to go before boarding time. Enjoying our warm tea and a cheese sandwich, we watch the people rushing by. They all look so busy and serious, and I wonder if it is because they are nervous like us. Time flies, and before I know it we are sitting in a narrow chair in our aeroplane somewhere over the English Channel. A friendly stewardess offers us a light lunch. Everything feels so sophisticated. Not really our world, but we nevertheless enjoy all the attention.

After landing at Zurich airport, we need to struggle to find out where to go to pick up our suitcases. We decide to just follow the crowd. I am sure they all need to do the same as we. And there she is. On the other side of customs, Sue is waiting for us with the kids. The three of them are standing with bright smiles on their faces and waving to us. Little David is too small to know what is going on. He is sitting comfortably in his pushchair. His large eyes are carefully consuming all that is going on around him. "Mum, Dad, you made it!" Sue runs over and hugs us. It feels so good to have my daughter back in my arms. I've missed her so much. "Let me take your trolley. I've got the car outside," she says, slowly loosing her grip. "Don't be silly! I'll push the trolley," Bill insists. "But let's first say hello to this bunch. Gosh, you have all grown," Bill kneels down and opens his arms to Matthew and Kathy. Both charge towards him and hug their Granddad, nearly knocking him backwards onto the shiny floor.

We drive through the city of Zurich and then through a dark woodland area leading to the canton of Zug. Cantons are the equivalent to counties in England, as Sue explains. Their flat is in a small village called Hünenberg, which means the hill of the giants translated into English. It's a nice village on the top of a hill. A lot of construction is going on. The area seems to be developing. Many beige-coloured flats are being built. In Switzerland, it is quite common to live in flats instead of houses. They are nicely built with the best materials, and double-glazing against the cold winters.

The next day, after settling down, Sue takes me to the village centre to buy some groceries. Bill stays home with the children. Walking down the street to the centre, I'm all chatty, telling my daughter all the stories happening around Church Stretton. Sue has made a list of all she needs, and spends some time finding the right translation into German.

She's nervously clinging to the list while we stand in front of the butcher's shop. She doesn't seem to be listening to my talking. "Mum, you will have to be quiet now. I need to concentrate to get this right, or we will end up with the wrong things," she absently tells me, without looking up from her list. I nod, without daring to say another word. All is well organised inside the shop. The fresh meat is displayed in a refrigerated glass display. A chubby butcher with a white apron and pink cheeks smiles at us. He says something I can't understand, but I guess it must mean something like "How can I help you?" Sue looks up from her list and greets him. She carefully reads what she needs, one word after the other. The butcher nods, and reaches for the minced meat. Sue relaxes. "Ah, I got that right," she nods back to him with a grateful smile.

After the butcher, we go on to a small supermarket. Everything is a bit easier here. We can pick the goods we need by ourselves.

"Everything is incredibly expensive here," Sue tells me on our way home. "We thought we would be able to save more with the salary Chris gets. But it all gets eaten up by the high cost of living," she adds. "But it's a lovely place. Look how clean the streets are." She points to the pavement in front of us. "And everything is so organized. You need the right coloured bin bags, and you are only allowed to wash on certain days at clearly defined time," she giggles. "It is beautifully clean and the people seem very friendly. It's quite special to be greeted every time a person passes you on the street," I join in. "Well you know. The people are very nice. But it is a bit strange. You are supposed to call people by their family name, like Mr Jones or Mrs Huwyler. You can only call them by their first name after they have permitted you to do so. This normally happens after you have met them a couple of times. It's like a little ceremony. You toast each other with a glass of wine, and then give permission to call each other by their first name. I'm not really used to that," she explains to me. "Well, that is odd, isn't it?" I agree. "I have made friends with some of the neighbours. Their children are the same age as ours. Valerie, one of our neighbours, is from Australia and has three children. I enjoy having somebody to talk to. My German lessons are going well, but it's still difficult to have a longer discussion in German. There are so many rules. It can get a bit frustrating," Sue smiles. "When will the children start school?" I ask. "After the summer break. Matthew will go straight to school. Kathy will join play school. The children start school quite late here. I hope they won't miss out too much. It will be difficult otherwise when we go back. But we think we should take the chance, and send them to the local school so they can learn proper German. The first half-year they will get some extra German lessons after class, so they can hopefully pick-up the language quickly. After that, we'll see how it goes," she smiles over to me with a slightly worried expression. "Don't worry love. Children learn quickly. It will be a big advantage for them to learn a second language," I calm her.

The following weekend, we all pile into the car. Chris has planned a trip up the mountain. If we are lucky, there will probably still be some snow at the top. We drive up winding, steep roads. The landscape slowly changes from a blooming summer green to a darker, stony look. Tall fir trees take the place of apple and cherry orchards. They stand closely together in groups, like giant statues guarding the open fields. Even though a light breeze is blowing, they don't seem to move an inch. Majestically they stand and patiently wait. Their dark green needles add a fearful look to them.

We park the car and walk up a gravel lane that takes us up to the summit. The air is wonderfully fresh. The cool breeze brushing against my skin is a refreshing change to the hot air in the valley. The meadows on both side of the path are filled with beautifully coloured flowers I've never seen before. I feel tempted to pick some. "Mum, you are not allowed to pick the flowers. They are protected!" Sue calls over to me, as if she could read my mind. Kathy, who is holding my hand, looks up at me with a sulk. "Never mind, we can pick some in Hünenberg when we are back. I have seen a lot of pretty ones close to the wood," I reassure her.

After a short walk, we reach the platform. From here you can see for miles. The view is fantastic. The blue sky, the surrounding mountains with their white tips and far down below the glistening lakes. Matthew and Kathy run off and explore the area, while Bill and I take a rest on a wooden bench. Inhaling the crisp air, we enjoy the panorama in front of us. I close my eyes for some moments. Picturing the surroundings, I remember a dream I once had as a child. In my dream I could fly and go to faraway places. Spreading my arms, I flew to mountain areas with fresh meadows and pretty flowers. And here I am. I have arrived in my dream world surroundings. Okay, I didn't fly, but nevertheless I am here. I can feel Bill putting his arm around me. I slowly lean back and enjoy his warmth. The cool breeze is drying the small glittering pearls on my forehead. It's a peaceful moment that I save deep in my heart. In the distance, I can hear the children playing. They are in their own little world. Discovering new things every moment of the day. It's a wonderful time. My brothers and I were always everywhere. Not missing anything and always happy. Looking back, time went so quickly. Now we are all grandparents. But as a child, you cannot wait for tomorrow to come. Hours can feel like forever. Waiting for my birthday or Christmas morning was torture. Sometimes I thought it would never happen. Today, I cannot keep up anymore. I am even starting to use my fingers to count my age. Closer to us, I can hear Sue and Chris talking to David. He is only just starting to walk and needs help. He is such a calm soul. Watching his brother and sister amble around him. He doesn't seem to be bothered. He will make his steps in his own time.

The breeze is picking up. I can feel the outer layer of my skin slowly start to go cold. The feeling is distracting, and takes me back to the now. Opening my eyes, I once again enjoy the view in front of me. The feeling of space and freedom mixes with sadness. Half of our visit is already over. "I didn't want to think about this yet," I tell myself. But I can't stop it. It's already there. The thought of going home fills me with emptiness. I don't know when I will see my daughter again. The children will be off to school in a couple of weeks, so they will not have the option to come back to England for visits soon. They will celebrate Christmas in Switzerland. Chris' Mum and maybe his brother will be visiting. A year could easily pass until we see them again.

David will definitely be walking by then, and Matthew and Kathy will be talking in a language we don't understand.

Bill gently kisses my forehead as if to calm my thoughts. I sigh and smile up to him. "Lets take a walk around before we go back down," he suggests with a smile. Taking my hand, he helps me to my feet.

In the following days, we take more day trips to Lucerne, and to an ancient Swiss village up the mountains. We also spend time in the city of Zug. It's a lovely and calm town with its own lake. The old town is built almost on the water, and is a joy to walk through. The cobbled alleys lead us past little shops and restaurants. Sue tells us that a part of the old town sunk into the lake in the 18th century. When freshly arriving in Switzerland, they first stayed at a hotel right on the town square. Sue laughs. "It was a cold winter day when we went for our first walk along the lake. Kathy was trying to get closer to the swans. The slope leading into the water was covered with slippery green moss. I wasn't watching her for only a second and off she went. She slipped and fell into the cold water. That was a commotion. Luckily the water wasn't too deep, and our hotel was close." We all have to laugh, thinking of our little red haired girl sliding into the icy winter lake.

Time flies in Switzerland, and only too soon we are packing again. But this time it's much easier. I'm looking forward to our cottage and I'm anxious to see our garden. Hopefully all have survived! We have bought a lot of Swiss chocolate for our storage and to share with friends. The taste of the creamy brown squares is truly a treat. But my favourite conquest is a

Swiss cuckoo clock. It's a dark brown Swiss chalet with girls and boys in front dressed in traditional clothing. Whenever the clock strikes the full hour, a little door opens and the cuckoo sticks out its head and chirps the number of the hours.

Bill is anxiously checking our suitcases for the third time to be sure that all our pieces are in the right place and that nothing can potentially get damaged. He is nervous, anyone could see that from a mile. "I'm sure everything is okay, Bill," I casually try to calm him. Bill ignores my words. "We need to fill the little spaces in between the piles with socks and underwear. That will stop everything sliding around. The suitcases are in for quite a rough time you know," he explains, without looking up from what he is doing. Bill is quite an expert when it comes to packing. He successfully rolls jumpers and shirts to prevent them from getting creased. I don't know where he learned that, maybe in the army. The soldiers were constantly living out of backpacks. "Mum, Dad, how's it going?" Sue appears in the doorway with David hanging on her hip. "I guess we should leave in about 30 minutes to make sure you have enough time. Would you like a cup of tea?" she asks us. "That would be lovely dear," I smile at her. "But I'm not sure if your Dad has time. He is too busy finding socks and underpants to fill the gaps," I smirk. "There, there, I just want your cuckoo clock to arrive safely. A cup of tea would be lovely. I guess I am finished here. No more gaps to be filled." He pats the pile of clothes and carefully closes the lid.

The three of us sit around the coffee table. David is playing with some Lego on the ground. "I'd better call Matthew and Kathy," Sue steps out onto the balcony. Five floors down, Matthew and Kathy are playing with the neighbour's children on the lawn. "They will be up in a minute. How's your tea?" Sue asks us. "Oh it's good, nothing like a cup of tea," I smile. "Well, it's not really like the English tea, is it? Unfortunately, they don't have many English products in the stores. There are a lot of things I miss," Sue sighs. "When do you think you will be over next?" I ask. "Earliest next summer. That will be the first large break the children have from school." Sue doesn't look very happy hearing her own words. "We'll see you again in a year's time" I say aloud to myself. "You will be talking by then, David," David looks up at me with big eyes and a red Lego brick in his hand. Behind us, the front door opens and little footsteps run in. "Close the door please," Sue calls to the kids. Little steps run back and the front door is slammed closed, which makes us jump. Kathy has vanished off to the toilet. With the bathroom door open, she is complaining about why she needs to be home. She cannot understand. Matthew is off into the kitchen for some juice. "Both of you wash your hands. We will be leaving in five minutes," Sue orders. "I'd better get David ready," She picks up David and vanishes off into the second bathroom. Bill and I are left sitting in the living room. "Well, I guess it's time to go, Mollie. I'll get our bags. Do you have everything you need?" Bill kindly asks me. "Yes, I am ready." A wave of sadness presses against my chest and makes me swallow.

After a 50 minute drive, we arrive at the airport. Sue helps us find the check-in counter and accompanies us to the departure gate. The sad, heavy feeling rapidly builds against my chest. Frantically, I try to keep up swallowing to ease the pressure. But I am too slow. My eyes are watering. A full year without seeing my daughter and our grandchildren. We have never been apart for so long. I cannot wait for their two years of Switzerland to be up and for them to come home for good. Next to me, I can see that Bill is having the same fight. He is trying to distract himself by repeatedly going through our travel documents. Sue hasn't noticed us getting emotional yet. She is too busy keeping her three children together.

The departure gate is the furthest we can all go together. "Well, here we are," Bill swallows. "Mum, Dad, it has been so great to have you over. It has meant so much to me," Sue grabs our hands. "I will very much miss you both." Sue's eyes water. "Come here my dear," Bill embraces his daughter. His face has gone all pink. While they hug each other, I kneel down to the children and hug each one. "Now, you be good kids and help Mummy, right!" I order them with a big kiss. After quickly wiping away his tears, Bill joins me. Getting back to my feet, I know I have still the hardest goodbye in front of me. Sue is brightly smiling at me. "Don't worry Mum. Time will fly. You'll see. We'll soon be back." Sue hugs me hard. Her build is so fragile, I'm worried that I will hurt her if I hug her back the same way. "You do a great job, my love. I will miss you terribly. You know that." I reassure her. One last time we stand together, before Bill and I walk through the departure check. On the other side, we stand in front of the thick glass wall and wave. Matthew and Kathy run to the glass and frantically wave back. Sue stands with David in her arms, looking a little lost and alone. From distance, her slim build is even more visible. Her blonde hair is shining in the bright light. I don't know how she does it, and from where she gets her energy. After wiping her eyes, she gently waves back and points us out to David. A hard knot builds in my throat. "What if I never see her like this again?" I ask myself. I'm confused by my own thoughts. Why shouldn't I see her like this? Discharging my odd thought, I search for Bill's hand to hold.

Sitting in the plane back home, Bill and I don't talk too much. We both enjoy the quiet to sort all the experiences we have made over the past two weeks. My strange thought of not seeing my daughter the way we just left her again nags me. "Why am I thinking something like that?" I ask myself. "It's a long time until I see her again. That is probably why I am worried," I try to calm myself. I turn to the plane's window and stare out into the white clouds, and let my thoughts drift to our cottage and garden. A hardly visible new wrinkle remains on my forehead. But I don't notice. I have cleverly distracted myself with my flower obsession.

CHAPTER FIFTEEN

The two years in Switzerland have passed, but our family didn't come home. Chris was offered an extension of his contract. Sue wanted to come back, but the family was making a lot of new experiences and enjoying the country. The children were learning the language and slowly settling down at school. So they decided to stay on for two more years.

Bill and I were planning our next trip over to Switzerland. We haven't actually booked anything yet, but we are trying to find one to two weeks that would match us all well. It makes us nervous to leave our home for so long. We are just not used to it.

After a walk down the village, Bill is resting in his armchair reading the newspaper. I have decided to dust our rarely-used sitting room. Not really something I enjoy doing. Just as I am getting on with it the ring of our phone makes me jump. Carefully, I lay down the china ornament in my hand. I'm glad to get away from the dusting for a few minutes. Walking to the telephone, I realize that Bill hasn't moved. He must be comfortably snoozing or is too tired to get up. The telephone has just rung a third time when I pick it up. "Cooke," I announce. "Mum, it's me. How are you doing?" Sue asks at the other end. "Sue, I wasn't expecting you. What a nice surprise. We are well, thank you. We were just down the village. Now Bill is resting in his armchair and I am dusting some of our pieces in the sitting room. Nothing interesting. How are you?" I ask. "Oh I'm okay Mum. I was wondering if you and Dad have already found a date to come to Switzerland," she asks. "No, not yet. Sometime early summer would be nice, right?" I ask. "Would it be possible for you to come a little earlier, Mum? I have been to the doctor. Um, I found a lump in my left breast. It has been checked and it's not good. I have a malignant tumour. It's breast cancer, Mum." Sue explains. I'm lost for words. I don't know what to say. Sue has breast cancer? "Mum, are you there?" She asks, a little confused. "Oh yes, I'm lost for words. What does it mean?" I ask. "Well, it means I will have to have it cut out," her voice weakens, and I can hear her swallow. But she can't control her fear. Her voice breaks and I can hear her weep. "They are going to take my breast off, Mum." I can hear her clap her hand over her mouth to quieten her scream. I can see myself in the mirror across from me. I'm standing there like a ghost. Not moving an inch. Our innocent, carefree years flash past my eyes. A deep crack in the floor is separating us from them. I take a step to try to keep my balance. One foot is on each side of the threatening abyss. "Mum," I can hear my daughter calling me. "Yes, my dear. Of course we can come earlier. When is the operation planned for?" I ask her, letting my survival mode take over. On the other end I can hear her clearing her nose. "In two weeks' time," her voice trembles. "Is it that far progressed?

Don't they have any other options first?" I ask. "No, it's too large. They want to be sure not to leave any parts of the tumour that could further infect my body," she explains. "I just can't understand. You were always such a healthy girl. But I guess we have to be glad they found it early enough. Try not to worry, my dear. You will be okay. You're so strong and Chris loves you so much, no matter what." I feel silly trying to calm her. I would like to close her into my arms and take all bad things onto myself. My daughter is too young to have to go through this. It isn't fair. "Thank you, Mum. I just can't think of what I will look like with only one breast. I don't dare even thinking of what I will look like for him." Her voice breaks once again. I can hear her tears running down her face. "Will you talk to Dad and let me know when you come over, okay?" She sobs. "Of course my love. I'll talk it through with Dad and call you tomorrow. I'm so sorry! You will make it, do you hear. Everything will be all right," I reassure her. "Yes Mum, it's just the shock. We'll hear from each other tomorrow. I love you!" It goes quiet on the other end. "I love you too, and hug the children for us. I'll talk to you tomorrow." After I have put the receiver down, I stand for a moment and absently knead my fingers, lost in thought.

Two weeks later, Bill and I are in Switzerland. Sue's operation has gone well. The doctors believe they have successfully taken out the cancer. A large scar marks her breast, and she'll need a lot of time to rest and heal. The vicious medication additionally tires her. The children know that Mummy isn't well and needs a lot of sleep, but they don't understand the scale. Sue, Chris, Bill and I have decided it's best to leave it this way. They are just too young, and we are all convinced that soon she will be on her feet and well again. And how would you explain cancer to a four, seven and nine year old? It was hard enough explaining it to ourselves. I just couldn't understand why it had chosen Sue to be its carrier. She didn't smoke and hardly drank. She had always been a healthy girl and hadn't done anything wrong in life. There was no reason at all for her to be punished with this burden. But it's rare that somebody deserves to be punished. Life makes its own way without explaining why.

Sitting on their balcony, I stare out to the playground. Children are playing some game like hide-and-seek. They are so carefree. Running up and down the small hills and hiding behind bushes, rocks and trees. Life is kissing them all. All is wonderful until they need to go to bed. And going to bed is only terrible because they need to leave life behind them for some hours. Who knows what they will miss?

The children's colourful shirts go fuzzy in front of my eyes, blend together and gain distance. Their cheers and laughter sound far away, as if there was cotton wool in my ears. I allow my thoughts to take me away. My daydream leads me back to England. All is black and white, like in an old television film. Sue is a little blonde angel and Bill and I have lost our wrinkles. We are out in the green, playing catch. Our shoes are lying next to our tartan picnic blanket, all mixed together. The grass beneath our feet is fresh and luscious. Its shiny surface nearly makes it slippery to run on. The sunlight's reflection on the surface of the grass looks like millions of diamonds are scattered over the lawn. The three of us are running after each other in turns. We are so happy and full of joy for our lives.

Bill happily collapses on the picnic blanket. "Ah, I can't anymore, I need a break," he pants. "Mummy, Mummy, look, I'll jump onto Daddies' tummy," Sue excitedly screeches. And off she goes. Running as fast as she can, she spreads her arms. I can only see her blonde curls charging towards poor Bill. Like a wrestler in the ring, she pounces down onto him. "Ouch, got ya," Bill groans, while twirling his eyes to fight against the sudden pain of being squashed by his own little girl. I cannot help but laugh, and run over to join them. The three of us lie on the blanket and stare up into the sky. There are no limits and no ceiling that could stop our love growing for each other. The bright sunlight blinds us. Cuddled together, we close our eyes and enjoy the sun's touch, the smell of fresh grass and most of all, the feeling of being together.

"Mum? Are you okay?" Sue carefully sits down besides me on the balcony. I can see that she is trying to cover her pain. "Oh, I must have dozed off," I explain, rubbing my eyes. "The three of them are tiring, aren't they," says Sue, absent-mindedly staring down to the playground. "Its not too bad. Are you going to manage my love?" I ask, watching her. Bill and I are travelling back home in two days. "Somehow we always manage, and Chris' office is close. Luckily we have some nice neighbours, and Chris is talking to his Mum. So Edith may be over soon. You don't need to worry Mum, it's going upwards from now on, the worst is behind me. It's just the scar that hurts when I move," she smiles over to me, but her eyes are glazed. "You know what, I might just have a lie down before everyone comes home for dinner." She slowly stands up again, trying not to bite her lips, and vanishes into the flat. Left alone, I stare out into the blue again. I feel torn inside. My daughter is in pain and needs help, even though she doesn't admit it. But Bill and I need to go back. We have nobody to take care of our home. I feel as if I'm deserting her. The thought that Edith may be over soon calms me a little. Looking over to the other homes, I pray that the neighbours will help my angel.

The next summer, the family is over to visit us in England. Bill and I couldn't wait to see them all. We had spent months and months alone at our cottage. Just living our normal life. Going up the hill and down the village. Barbara visited us now and then. My brother's daughter has become a dear friend to us. I enjoy my time with her, having someone female to talk to. She does partly fill the gap that my mother left.

Bill and I have spent days preparing the cottage for the children. All the valuables have been carefully cleared away into the storage room. The small back bedroom is set up with two single beds and one small folding bed. The room is packed. We can hardly turn. Sue's room has been tidied up and offers quite some space for Sue and Chris. The children will be spending four weeks with us, and Bill has made a list of outdoor activities. The excitement we feel is nearly making us burst. They'll be arriving any minute. They're coming by car. This way, they have enough space for all they need, and can travel around in England and load enough of their long-missed goods to take home.

Luckily, Chris loves to drive his car, and doesn't mind the travelling time.

A knock at the door indicates their arrival. Both Bill and I quickly open the front door to greet them. All five of them are standing in front of our house with big smiles on their faces. For the next minutes, a lot of hugging and kissing goes on. I feel so happy to see them all. Tears blur my sight.

During the following days, I cannot help to notice that Sue hasn't got her shine back. The usual glow around her has gone. She is happy, smiley and all. But something is missing. She reassures me that her scar has fully healed and isn't causing any problem. At first I think that it is maybe the tiring travel by car that she needs to recover from, but, as the days go on, nothing changes. I decide to keep my observations for myself. I don't want to worry anybody, or disturb the happy time we're spending together.

The children are a joy. They love going up the wood, down the valley and on Bill's excursions. Whenever they have a free moment, the three of them are off to explore the woodland. They remind me of my brothers and myself. We loved to be out in the nature. There was always so much to do and discover.

Sue's best friend, Sue, has two daughters the same ages as Matthew and Kathy. One of the daughters, Bethany, has become a good friend to Kathy. Kathy even goes to school with her. She seems to like the English school system, and cannot wait to be up in the morning and be picked up. After school, she regularly walks the neighbour's dog up the valley. I think she takes after her mother in her love of the

English country. For Sue and Chris, it's a joy to see her feel comfortable and looking forward to be able to go to school. It hasn't been too easy for the children to find their place in Switzerland. Not speaking the language has made the situation difficult for them in a country village. Children can be so brutal to each other.

On a late afternoon, I'm standing in the kitchen podding the peas I picked in the garden. Chris joins me at the kitchen counter. "Gosh Mollie, your china and brass collections have grown since we were last here." Surprised, I look up at him. Trust Chris to notice that, I think to myself. Luckily he doesn't know that I have cleared a lot into the storage room, I calm my thoughts. "You think so?" I naively ask him. "You know me, I can't walk past a pretty piece," I smile. "I am sure this isn't all. Mum and Dad have surely moved a lot of pieces to the back room," Sue smiles with a wicked look while entering the room. Damn, trust them both, I think to myself, feeling caught. "I'm a collector," I defend myself. "So do you also collect rubber bands, Mum," Sue gestures to a drawer next to the kitchen sink. "We are gardeners, and we need things like that! Now you watch it or I won't lend you one when you're in need. Our parents taught us to be economical. You don't just through things away. I know that your generation thinks a little differently, but that's not how we are," I justify myself. "Don't worry Mum, I'm just having a little fun with you. But don't overdo it or we soon won't fit into the house anymore," she smiles. "Kathy needs her hair washed. Do you think Dad would do that for her?" She asks, changing the subject. "Sure, you know he loves doing that," I'm glad to change the subject. Bill is so calm, has lovely soft hands and the patience of a saint. He is the perfect hair washer. Not like me. I'm not patient with things like that, and not gentle enough.

"Great, I'll see where they are," Sue turns to leave for the garden. "I saw Kathy go out with her Barbie. She loves those elegant dolls," I tell Sue. "I know, that must be a Lee thing she has," Sue turns and smiles at Chris. "Yep, looks like some genes of my Mum have made their way through," he winks back at her. "Bill is out there too, with the boys. They are helping him with the garden," I add.

The family weeks soon draw to an end. On the last night, after the children are in bed, the four of us sit together around the Rayburn. "Mum, Dad, I'll be starting a chemo therapy when we are back in Switzerland. Before we left for England, I went for a check-up at the hospital. They found new cancer cells," Sue explains in a hurry, without looking up at us. She is nervously kneading her fingers. Her shoulders are hanging and she is leaning forward, bending her back in an insecure looking way. All her energy seems to have left her. In shock, I just stare at her. Even though I'd seen the indications, I'd pushed them far away from me. Thinking she would have told me, or that I would have noticed a more tangible sign. But she hadn't, and I didn't want to see. Knowing would have made it real and would have given the cancer its space. A rage of anger builds up inside of me. On the one hand because I hadn't been told, on the other hand because this cancer had crept back into my family. "How dare it! How dare it!" I repeat in my mind. After a few moments of silence, Sue shyly looks up at me through her dark lashes. I feel lost looking into her green eyes. All the blood drains from my face and fear overcomes me. Fear of the coming months and fear of what is to be. My only child will be fighting for her life, and I don't know how to help her. Bill finds his voice first. "I don't understand. They took it out. You're okay!" He kind of explains to himself. "Why didn't you tell us earlier?" He looks at his daughter with a serious expression on his face. "I'm sorry Dad! I'm sorry Mum! I didn't tell you because I didn't want the news to spoil our summer together. I didn't want it to be a part of our joint time. We just wanted to have a nice time with you. Not have to think and talk about it all the time. Have a break before it gets serious again. It meant a lot for me to be able to leave it back in Switzerland," she explains with a soft voice. With every word she says, I believe I can see her grow again. Her back has straightened and she can look us in the eyes again. Inwardly, she is building herself up through her words. Getting ready for her battle. The battle of her life.

"Mum?" She looks at me. "Are you okay?" She gently asks. I search for words, for clever things to say, but none come to my mind. "Um, I don't know what to say, my dear. This is a shock for all of us. I just don't understand," the last word hardly makes its way out. My voice fails, and heavy tears drop down onto my lap. The shock, the worries of the past year, the fear for the future and the powerlessness overcome me all at once. "I just don't understand why you," I carry on between deep sobs. "This isn't fair, it should be me, not you. You are too young and you have three children who need you," I try to dry my eyes with my hanky. "Come here," Bill joins me on my sitting chair and lays his arm around me. "Look at me. I'm crying and getting comforted. That's not right." I feel silly and ashamed because of my outburst. "It's okay Mum, it's the shock and you're my Mum. Mums worry, that's part of their job," she reassuringly smiles at me. "So, what's the procedure, what's going to happen once you are back?" I ask. "Well, once we are back, I will be going to the hospital for chemo twice a week. We need to see how I take it. The effects are different with everyone," she explains, looking over to Chris. He hasn't said anything all the time. His worried expression says everything though. He reaches over and takes her hand. "Don't worry, you'll be fine. We all will be fine. It doesn't matter what happens, I'm with you all the way. In good times and in bad times, that's what we promised," he reassures her. Sue swallows hard. "I'm afraid. Afraid what will happen to me. Will I be able to look after the children? They are so young and need me. Look at little David. He is so small. Matthew needs a lot of love. Even though he is the eldest, he still needs me to help him find his way and be certain of himself. And Kathy, she needs guidance and the feeling of being safe and looked after. It's not easy for them in Switzerland. The school system is unclear to us and they don't seem to get the same fair chance as the local children. They need to fight for themselves over and over again," Sue explains with a worried expression on her face. "We don't need to think of that. It'll be fine. The chemo will do its job and the local council have offered us help for the time you're in hospital. You'll be well supported," Chris tries to calm her. "You are right. We shouldn't be thinking of the worst. A couple of months and all will be over," she smiles at us. But it's not a happy, self assured smile.

We stay up for some time and talk about all that will happen.

In bed, I turn to Bill. "I wish we weren't so far away. They should have been coming back to England by now," I grumble. "Looking at all the medical treatment she needs, it's probably best if she can stay where her treating doctor is. He knows her medical story best," Bill explains, taking off his wristwatch and laying it on his bedside table. "Yes, probably. But Chris is so busy at work and the three children are quite a handful. What if she isn't well?" I ask. "They'll be getting household support from the council and they have some nice neighbours in the area. If the worst comes to worst, we can go over. But we're not the youngest anymore and it's not that easy for us to keep up with the three of them. And we can't leave the house for too long," Bill looks at me with a guilty expression. "Now we just need to stay calm and wait, and see how she takes the treatment. Our girl is a strong one. We know that." He kisses my forehead. "Let's get some sleep. All will look better in the morning." He lays his arm around me and pulls me close. His warm body lets me relax a little. But I don't fall asleep immediately. The discussion goes through my mind again and again. After what could have been hours, I fall into a restless sleep.

In my dream, I'm walking along a dark and dirty corridor. It's not a place I feel at ease in. I want to get out and walk as quickly as my short legs will take me. But the corridor doesn't end. I stretch out my arms so my hands can feel along the surfaces of both walls on either side to try and find a door leading outwards. The walls are uneven and damp. The surface is sticky and an unhealthy texture gathers beneath my hands. I can feel slimy filth make its way under my nails. Beneath my feet, the gravel makes each step uneasy. I'm afraid I'll slip and fall into the unseen. My fast pace and the damp, thick air makes me sweat. Running out of breath, I'm forced to slow down. My panting echoes through the tunnel. Slowly, I keep on walking. The gravel beneath my feet crunches with every step. Every now and then, a pebble escapes the pressure of my foot and bounces off the wall with a thud. But there is something else, I'm sure. There is hardly-to-be-heard whispering. It sounds like it's coming out of the walls. I turn to one side and try to spot what I believe I'm hearing. My eyes adjust to the dark. The wall is a shiny olive green. Looking down at my hands, I realize the extent of my situation. My hands have turned to the same dirty green, and the tip of my nails have coloured black. I quickly wipe my hands on my skirt. A rotten smell fills the air. "It doesn't go away!" I hear a quiet voice whisper. The words are followed by a dirty laugh. "Once it's here, it's here to stay. You will see." I still cannot make out where the words are coming from. I look up and down the wall. I believe I can see something moving on the ground. The smell of sulphur tickles my nose. A match is lit. A small green figure appears in the light of the flame. "We don't like the brightness. This is only for you. We want you to know who we are," the thing grins, and shows its dirty teeth. Its large eyes scan me. In the dark behind the thing, I believe I can see more eyes blinking. The things are quickly filling the area. More and more eyes appear in the dark. "Who are you? What do you want?" I ask, finding my voice. "It's not about who we are or what we want. There are no when's or why's in our world. We just are," it laughs. The match has burnt down and starts to sizzle when coming into contact with the thing's shiny long fingers. All goes dark again and I hear a faint rustling noise. The air clears. I'm sure I'm all alone again. Carefully, I take a step forward. I want to be out of this tunnel.

In bed, I turn from one side to the other and stretch my hands from my body. A few broken words escape my lips. "I want to be out of here. Get me out of here!" I turn once again and rest against Bill's back. His warmth calms my restless sleep.

CHAPTER SIXTEEN

The chemotherapy took its toll. Sue was in and out of the hospital, and kept us informed by phone. Luckily, she wasn't feeling too sick and didn't lose her hair. Even though it sounds petty in such a circumstance, I have to admit I'm very much relieved about this. After losing her breast, I couldn't imagine what it would be like for a young woman to then also lose her hair. To look at herself every day in the mirror and additionally worry about how her husband may see her. Not feeling like a woman anymore, but only like a very ill person. I am grateful that at least this is not the fact.

But I didn't feel sure she was really telling us everything. My feeling was more that she didn't want to worry us too much, and was therefore keeping information to herself.

Christmas came and left without much change in our lives. On the 31st of December, Bill came home with a bottle of champagne. Beaming all over his face, he walked into the cottage and proudly presented his buy on the kitchen counter. "I thought we should celebrate the New Year, probably with champagne," his cheeks are pink with excitement. "You know, we should welcome the New Year. We have a lot of hopes and wishes. So we should do it right," he explains, without letting go of the bottle. I cannot help but smile. Bill and I have always been careful with money. We rarely treated ourselves to something. On the one hand, we were happy with the way things were and didn't need much. On the other, we had been brought up in difficult times. You had no choice than to be pennywise. "You're right! We definitely should. We are asking the New Year for a lot. That it takes care of our only child. That it makes sure she's well and can live a fair portion of life," I agree. My last words make my eyes go watery. Bill lets go of the bottle and walks over and embraces me. He digs his face into my hair. "She will be okay! She will be okay!" His last word is only a sob. I can feel his tears wetting my hair. His grip around me strengthens. I'm close to feeling squashed. But I let him be. I can feel his pain and fear. We just stand there and hold each other, and let the time pass.

We open the champagne for dinner. The dry bubbly taste is a treat. I can feel the little bubbles pop all the way down into my tummy. It's like tiny butterflies opening their wings for one or two beats. A lovely warm feeling spreads out inside of me and I feel relaxed and comfortable.

Shortly before midnight, we fill a new glass each with the golden fluid. Through the backdoor, we step out into the garden. It's dark. The light from our living room shines out through the back window onto the concrete path leading through our garden. Two large fires guard the entrance to our pride. All is calm in our garden. Far away, somewhere down in the village, we can hear that there must be lots of people out on the streets. Ready to celebrate and greet the New

Year together with a lot of laughter and joy. And so would we. Not so much with laughter and joy, but with hopes and wishes. To our left we can see the steeple of the church. We stand and wait in silence, holding our glass in the one hand and each other's hand in the other. And there it is. The church clock chimes 12 times. The New Year has arrived. We look at each other and inwardly speak our prayers. Without speaking a word, we clink our glasses and enjoy the warm bubbly feeling run through us. Bill lays his arm around me and, for a moment, we look up to the stars in the deep black sky. I cannot stop myself from shivering. The cold is soaking through the last layer of my clothes. "Come on, we'd better get back in before you catch a cold," Bill says, and leads me back to the cottage.

This night, I quickly fall into a deep sleep. In my dreams I again hear quiet whispering and dirty laughter. The sound takes me back into the dark tunnel without doors. I can feel the gravel crunch beneath my feet as I turn and try to adapt to the dark. My arm brushes the damp wall. Quickly, I try to wipe off the slimy texture with my hand. But my hand is already wet and dirty. It feels as if I am only spreading the slippery mass over my arm. A foul smell reaches my nose. Down close to my feet, I can hear laughter. "It's growing. Didn't we tell you?" I hear an evil voice whisper. "Yes we did! Yes we did!" I hear from the other side. Deep fear builds and spreads over my body. I don't know what to do. I cannot move. I do not want to touch anything more. I want these voices to stop.

In bed, I turn from one side to the other, trying to wake myself up. But I am in too deep.

The slippery walls around me start popping. "Oh. Oh. Here we go! It's tickling," the voices whisper to each other, followed by deep laughter. Beneath me, the ground bubbles like an upset stomach. I lose my balance and crouch down. In fear, I close my eyes and pray. Again the ground lifts. Little pebbles roll away from my feet. It feels like I am standing on a balloon that is being blown-up. Shortly before it bursts, it sinks down again. Laughter from all sides rings out. "More, more! Yes, again, again!" is shouted out around me. I squeeze my eyes closed even more and embrace myself tightly. Burying my head in my lap, I let my tears run. The temperature in the tunnel swells. I can hardly breath. Sweat runs down my back.

"Mollie. Mollie. Wake up!" Bill shakes me. "You are soaking wet. We need to get you changed," Bill is looking down at me with a worried expression. "Oh, it was a bad dream. All these little voices and the foul smell. The air was thick and hot. I couldn't get myself to wake up," I explain a little confused. "Well, you're awake now. Everything is okay. Now let's get you some fresh clothes," Bill kisses my forehead and slips out of bed. The fresh winter air and my soaked night-gown make me shiver. Bill fetches a fresh gown out of the drawer. I quickly change my clothes and curl into Bill's lap. He holds me tight, making me feel safe and warm. But something is not in order. My dream told me. I decide to call Sue the next day. I need to know what's going on.

The other day, after breakfast, I sit down in the hallway and dial Sue's number. After a couple of rings, Chris picks up the phone. "Chris Lee," he answers. "Chris, hi, here is Mollie," I greet him. "Hi Mollie, how are you doing? Happy New Year!" Chris replies. "Happy New Year too! We are well, thank you. It's very cold here, but I guess it's the same over in Switzerland, right?" I ask. "Yes it is. But at least our double-glazing is doing its job. In Switzerland you can more or less walk around the flat in your underpants all year if you want," he replies with a laugh. "Now that is a little bit too much information," I chuckle. "How are the kids doing?" I carry on. "They are all well, and happy with their Christmas presents. They have been out with the new bob sledge every day. We will need some new snow soon - the hill they slide down is getting its first brown patches," he tells me, sounding quite excited himself. Chris loves the winter sport options Switzerland offers. They have all learned to ski, and have been on ski holidays every winter. They have sent us pictures of them all in thick winter jackets and trousers on the snowy pistes. It all looks quite scary to me, but they seem to do well and get down the steep slopes in one piece. "That sounds exciting for them. Are you planning a ski holiday this year?" I casually ask. "Err, well it really depends on how Sue is doing I guess. I would like to, but, you know, we have to take it week for week at the moment. The side effects haven't been too bad so far. But they are going to put the dose up this year. They haven't been able to kill off the cells. The doctors are afraid they will further spread, so we have to act fast." All the excitement in his voice has vanished. He sounds worried. "But let me give you Sue. She will love to hear you." The line goes quiet, and I can hear Chris calling Sue in the distance. A few seconds later, Sue is on the line. "Mum, how are you? Happy New Year!" She cheers. "Hi my dear, happy New Year to you too! How are you?" I calmly ask her. "Oh, I'm doing okay. The chemo isn't quite doing its job though. The doctors have told me that we will need to increase the dose in the New Year, and also make some alternations to the medication. At least the side effects haven't been bad, so I'm hoping it will stay that way," she explains to me. "I'm also doing a radiation therapy. It's like having an X-ray. The treated area on my back, breast and abdomen is marked with a blue colour that doesn't go off for days. I look like the sheep up the Shropshire hills with the owners' colour mark on their white coat," she tries to laugh. "How are you feeling with all these treatments?" I ask her. "Um, as said, it's not too bad. I am quickly tired and I sometimes get an upset tummy. My lymph system seems to be working a bit slow. My feet tend to swell. But otherwise I can't complain," she explains to me in a business-like way. "Are you getting some help?" I carry on to ask. "Most of the time I can have the hospital appointments while the children are at school. Now and then help has been here from the council to keep the flat in order. But I'm really doing quite well, so don't need much support," Sue replies, sounding proud. "Mum, don't worry! It just takes a little time. How's Dad?" She asks. "Oh, he is fine. We treated ourselves to some champagne yesterday. That was nice. Christmas has been quiet. We had a roasted chicken instead of a turkey. It just would have been too much for only the two of us. Barbara visited us on Boxing Day. She is lovely," I tell her. "That sounds nice. Gosh it's been some years since we have celebrated Christmas in England. I do miss it. I would like to come home soon. It's difficult to get whole turkeys here," she complains. I can hear the children fighting in the background, Sue seems distracted. "Well, I'd better let you go. Sounds like you have a handful over there," the noise is even getting hard for me to listen to. "Oh, yes Mum. I'd better sort this out. Start thinking about whether you'd like to come over this summer, okay?" Sue asks me. "Yes, I will talk about it with Bill. Now take care and keep us informed, okay?" I order her. "Yes Mum, I will! Give Dad a kiss from me, will you. I love you Mum," Sue kindly ask me. "I will, my love. Say hi to all. I love you too," I reply. The line goes quiet and I hang-up the receiver. Still sitting on the chair, I absently study my nails. I don't know how I should classify the information I received.

Bill pops his head through the door leading to the living room. "Would you like a cup of tea?" He kindly asks. "Yes, that would be nice. I'll be right over," I smile back at him. Bill walks back into the living room. In the kitchen area, I can hear him pour water into the kettle. For another moment I just sit, and try to find some energy to move. The kettle is already boiling. I can hear the steam escaping from the spout, making a whistling noise. I listen to Bill's footsteps. He is walking back to the kitchen area. The cutlery drawer is opened and closed, followed by the cupboard where we store our cups. There is a gurgling noise of boiling water being poured into a china cup, followed by the sound of a spoon stirring the sugar. I know my time is up. I must move or Bill will be back any second and I don't want to be looked at strangely. I take a deep breath, stem my hands on my thighs and stand up.

Together, we sit down next to the Rayburn. The warmth does me good and I relax back into the chair. "How was your call?" Bill asks me. "Oh, it was good. Chris sounded excited and full of hope for a ski holiday. The kids are enjoying the snow and their Christmas presents. And Sue, well, she sounded okay. A little tired I would say and maybe a bit dull. But I guess that all hangs together," I try to explain, not only to Bill but also to myself. "How is the treatment going?" Bill carries on to ask. "The treatment so far hasn't brought the expected results. They are going to change the dose. And probably also increase the amount, as the doctors are getting worried the cells could quickly spread." Bill carefully listens to all my explanations. Going though all that was said gives me time to digest it and form my opinion.

"What do you think?" I ask Bill. Bill looks at me and strokes his hair back with his hand. "That they haven't found the right medication is disappointing. But then again, it does take time. We just have to wait. If she is independent and feeling okay most of the time, then that's good news, I think. Or at least a sign that it is not getting worse, don't you think?" Bill looks at me with a worried expression. "Um, I guess," is all I can really say. I think back to my last night's dream. Something is telling me that its not good. Or is it just my fantasy taking over? I shake my head at myself. "I shouldn't watch so much television," I tell myself. With this sentence, I lock away my worries in a faraway and dark place in the back of my mind. A storage place of my own that nobody can see and ask me to clear.

Spring knocks on our door and melts the little bit of snow we had in our garden. The fine white layer that was covering the died-down plants makes space for new to grow. But the things that we need to dig up and carry away also become obvious. Wrapped in a warm coat, I stroll through our garden. Here and there, snowdrops are sticking their heads to the sky. I think these small dainty flowers are so brave. They are nearly the smallest and still they are the first to show themselves. Even though there are still patches of frost and ice, they fight their heads through and let themselves be seen, spreading the thrill of anticipation for the coming spring. I gently pat some of the bare stems sticking out of the ground here and there. "You are all going to be fine soon. You will see!" I whisper to them. I inhale and watch small clouds of smoke travel though the air every time I exhale. They float so lightly away from me. It looks peaceful, even when it quickly dissolves and only see-through air is left. My fingers start to feel cold, but I carry on strolling through our garden. I need a little space. Indoors, Bill is on the phone to a travel agency. He is booking our flight to Switzerland for beginning of the summer. Our decision was quickly taken. Sue isn't doing very well. The new therapy is vicious and isn't providing the hoped-for results. The cancer cells have spread further and the hospital is treating various parts of her body simultaneously. Her daily fight and the medication are tiring her.

The situation makes me feel helpless. We just carry on living our lives. There is nothing that I feel I can offer, even though I would offer everything to see my girl well again. Every night, I plead to God to let me take her place. Please let her have a life. Let her see her children grow up. Let her carry us to our grave, and not the other way round. I punish myself for thinking the latter. How dare I even think of that!

Inside I am split. One half doesn't want to hear anything other than that she will be better soon. She is and always was a strong girl. No other scenario than seeing her healthy and happy with her children is realistic to me. On the other hand, I fear what still lies in front of us to reach this goal. How much can we all take? What happens if? I don't look at the "if". I don't want to know what "if" is.

On the telephone together, I don't know what to say anymore. What do you say? How do you keep hopes high when every other week the situation worsens? She has become more absent and numb, and Bill and I have therefore started exchanging more information with Chris. He is a dear son-in-law to us. I cannot even start to think what the situation is like for him. Being in a country that is still quite new to you. Not having many friends and no family close. Having to keep up at work, and see your wife suffering at home. Feeling helpless and at the mercy of the doctors.

A hot summer awaits us in Switzerland. The doctors have put Sue on a break from the treatment to give her body time to recover. The last treatment made her feet and abdomen swell terribly. She wasn't able to wear shoes anymore, and her tummy made her look as if she was highly pregnant. It had become very uncomfortable for her to move. Thanks to a reduced dose of medication, the swellings have gone and she is more alive and active again. But the disease has ravaged her. Her cheeks are pale and hollow. Her hair has gone colourless. There is no more shine. Her eyes are glazed and look uneasy. As if she is lost in thoughts, searching for something in her mind. Maybe due to the medication she was used to, and now misses. Or maybe it is the thought of her next fight against her demons.

The hot weather forced us to spend a lot of time on the shady balcony. Standing in the blazing sun just made us melt away, and we didn't want to wear Sue out by going on excursions on our behalf. The three of us were once again stretched out on the balcony sipping a refreshing ice tea when Sue had an idea. "Mom, Dad, let's go out tomorrow. I would like to leave the apartment and see something else. What do you think?" She asks us. Bill and I quickly glance at each other. Bill nods. "Sure dear, what would you like to do?" I ask. "Doesn't really matter. Something where we can feel a fresh breeze. This here is just too hot," she sighs. "How about a boat trip?" She asks, without giving us a chance to reply. "A boat trip sounds nice to me," Bill smiles. "Let's do that," I wink at her.

The next day, Sue dresses up in one of her favourite dresses. It's a white dress with little orangey-brown flowers on it. I hate to be noticing this, but the dress had got a little large for her. She has carefully braided her hair out of her face. Even though she cannot hide the illness and the pain she has endured, there is a glow of excitement around her. A carefree summer trip out with her parents and children. The outing means the world to her. The children are all excited to be going out, and Bill and I also get dressed-up in nice summery outfits. Without saying, we all knew the importance of this outing, and that this may be the last treat we could offer our daughter for a very long time.

After parking the car in the city centre, the six of us stroll down the street to the harbour. The heat of the sun is so intense I believe I can feel the asphalt melting beneath my shoes. It feels soft, as if I was walking on a foam-rubber kind of texture. Looking down at the road, I can see the heat slowly swirling just above the ground. It looks like a slow motion dance. Long, diffused arms and legs slowly moving up and down in synchronic perfection. Always just not touching the ground. A bewitching dance aimed to torment the earth's surface.

The heat has even quietened the children. They are following us as if in a trance, without grumbling, shouting or running off to discover something new.

The city's large passenger ship is ready for the cruise around the lake. Calmly it sits on the water, and waits for all the passengers to go onboard. After buying our tickets, we take a seat at the back of the ship, in the outside area. There is a Swiss flag hanging from a pole at the stern. The red of the flag, the blue of the water and the green of the hills around us provide a beautiful mix of strong colours. We slowly sail out of the harbour. It's a quiet day, and we are alone at the back of the boat. As the ship picks up its pace, a cool, refreshing breeze tickles our faces and dries our damp foreheads. The children excitedly run from one side to the other and watch the water foaming and hitting the sides of the ship. Bill is back and forth watching out for them, making sure none of them decide to climb too far over the railing. Sue and I just sit and enjoy the panorama, while letting the fresh breeze blow through our hair. We don't say too much. Now and then, Sue closes her eyes for a second and deeply enjoys the air blowing across her face. For a moment, it is as if she can let go of her demons and feel free. Opening her eyes again, she smiles at me openheartedly. "Ladies, say cheese please!" Bill calls. He is hidden behind his camera. Sue and I lay our arms around each other and smile into the camera.

Back home, I have exactly this picture of Sue and myself on the ship framed. Not that it is the best picture ever of Sue. No it isn't. You can see that she is ill. But it's the moment that we had together that means so much to me, and I want to be remembered of. The feeling of her being able to step out of her illness for a moment and just let go makes me feel happy for her.

CHAPTER SEVENTEEN

Returning back to England wasn't easy for us. We had to be realistic about what was happening. Sue's fight was tiring her and her reserves where shrinking. She'd taken too many hits, and her scars where not getting the time they needed to heal. Her enemy was vicious and without mercy. Every night I prayed for them to take me instead of her. And there they were again. After I fell asleep, they were back. Or maybe I was back, back in their dark tunnel. A place I didn't want to be.

In my sleep, I immediately know where I am. The damp, foul smell has become familiar to me. But it scares me nevertheless, and I'm afraid of what I may see this time. My eyes slowly adjust to the dark, and I slide my foot back and forth to test the ground beneath me. The gravel crunches and I feel some pebbles break away. Carefully, I stretch out my arms . The damp texture on the walls has grown. It feels like a bed of wet and slippery moss. I squeeze my eyes and lips closed in disgust. But I have no choice. It's too dark and I can't see enough to walk without guidance. I'm soon panting. It's damp and hot and it feels like I am walking upwards. Now and then I hear rustling noises and whispering. The sound is growing, and coming from all sides. I know it won't take long before they contact me. Sweat runs down my back. I brush across my itching arm with my hand. My skin feels sticky, like it's covered in a caramel icing. Confused, I gently stroke up my arm to my shoulder. It's all the way up. The gluey texture sticks to my fingers and pulls threads. I cannot make out the colour due to the dark, but inside I know the answer. It's the green texture that has spread from my hands all the way up my body. "Yes, yes, of course it is. You are learning, Mollie," a dirty voice laughs from the wall on my left. "But we won't be long. Don't worry. The path has become harder to walk along. And we are more, more every day. The more we get, the less time we have," the thing keeps on laughing. The rustling around us has become louder. Long shiny fingers with dirty nails light a match, and the smell of sulphur fills the air. Yellow teeth glow in the dim light. Two dark eyes scan me. "You ask too many questions. There are no answers. We just are," the thing smiles without a sound, studying me. "Where do I get out?" I mumble, frozen to the spot I'm standing on. The thing throws its head back in delight and a mucous layer breaks in its throat as it laughs. It throws the match to the ground. The flame dies between the grey pebbles. "Soon. Soon you will see!" The rustling noise around me quickly starts moving away from me. It sounds like thousands of little footsteps running in one direction. I know I'm all alone again. Carefully, I keep on walking until my surroundings fade away.

I don't feel rested the next morning. My mind is constantly spinning about my last night's dream.

I'm standing in our kitchen, washing up the cups from

our afternoon tea. Bill is in the garden. I can see him through the window, walking in and out of the shed. His shed is his pride and joy. His very own four walls. A man's world. I have no idea what he's doing. It looks like he is piling spare pots and his tools in and out. Who knows why? But we retirees have time. More time than enough, so from time to time we do things like that, and Bill loves order.

From my kitchen window I have a direct view of the birds' house in our garden. It's a passion of mine to watch the birds come for a bite. It makes the washing-up much easier to do. But no birds seem interested in our bread leftovers from breakfast today. It's kind of quiet and a grey fog is closing in. A cold shiver runs down my back. Suddenly, the phone rings in the parlour.

My heart misses a beat and I drop my teacup back into the tub. I'm startled. Bill stands by the shed and looks in my direction. He seems frozen by the shed door. Catching my breath again, I dry my hands while walking to the parlour and pick up the phone.

There is a short burst of noise. Then I hear Chris, my son-in-law. With a broken voice he tells me the news. My legs feel like they have sunk into the ground beneath me. I cannot move. We knew it was bad, but never even dared to think of what could be coming. The only words I can manage are: "We're coming." Nothing more needed to be said.

I stand clutching the dresser after replacing the receiver. My nails are digging into the soft polished wood. I can see myself go pale in the mirror in front of me. After what feels like hours, but must have only been seconds, I walk back into the kitchen. From the open backdoor I can see into the garden.

Bill is still frozen next to the shed. He doesn't seemed to have moved. Slowly, I walk out into the garden to join him. We just look at each other and Bill says: "We'd better pack."

The next day we are sitting at the airport, waiting to board our plane. My legs are dangling from the chair, which makes me feel a little silly. If I stretch my foot, I can just scratch the ground with the tip of my shoe. In front of us, the ground stewardess is standing behind her desk, looking into the computer screen with a blank expression. I wish they would hurry up and let us go. Nervously, I shift on my chair. Bill places his hand on mine to calm me. "We will leave soon. We're still on time. Don't worry, my love. She will wait for us," Bill looks over to me, with glazed eyes. With his other hand he fetches a crisp white handkerchief from his trouser pocket and wipes his eyes. We just look at each other. It's the first time one of us has said something like that. My eyes immediately blur up. I sniff and look down at my shoes. I don't know what to say. I just hold on tight to Bill's hand in my lap.

During the flight, we can hardly swallow down the sandwich we are served. Both of us leave most of it untouched on our trays. We land punctually in Zurich. Chris is waiting for us at the arrival area. He looks tired. Dark circles surround his eyes making him look older than he is. "Bill, Mollie, here I am," he waves to us. "Chris!" We wave back and quickly walk towards each other. "It's good that you could make it so quickly," he explains, helping us with our luggage. "The ambulance picked her up two days ago. She fell into a coma yesterday. She just didn't know what she was doing anymore. She was getting her medication mixed-up and I found her trying to brush her teeth with my shaving cream. I hid her medication to prevent her taking too much without knowing. She got very upset about this. I would even say aggressive. The doctors thought it was best for her to be taken back to hospital. She was too weak to walk, so they carried her out of the apartment on a stretcher," he explains, and I can see a tear drop from his eyes and hit the shiny airport floor. He hesitates, and wipes his nose with the back of his hand. For a moment he pauses, and I can see the fight within him. Instinctively I embrace him. Chris digs his head into my shoulder. A shiver runs through his body, and tears of deep sadness and despair release themselves. "The children were there. I don't know what they have realised. I haven't been able to tell them," he tries to explain between bitter sobs. "Sue wished them a good day at school. That was all. She couldn't hold them a last time," he carries on. "They are at school now, and can do their homework at the neighbours' house." He straightens himself, getting back control. "We'd better get on our way. She wasn't good this morning." He reaches back for one of the suitcases and shows us the way.

45 minutes later we are at the hospital. They have given Sue a bright single room with view of the lake. She is lying in bed with her eyes closed. Her skin is pale and her cheeks have hollowed even more since we saw her a few weeks ago. A drip is providing her with the necessary fluids. Now and

then, a nurse enters the room and injects additional medication. The medication is not to fight her demons, but to help her be with them. Her fight is over. The demons have won this battle. It's now all about making her feel comfortable, leaving her earthly body to them and finding her new path after this life.

The three of us sit around her bed and wait. I hold her hand and inwardly speak to her. "Sue, my love. I know you can hear me. You are the light of my life. I'm so sorry that I can't take this from you. It should be me. Not you, not you. You are too young. You have too much in front of you. I'm so sorry!" Tears run down my face. "If only I could come with you, my love." In my mind, I go back to the birth of Sue. "You were such a beautiful girl. I will never forget the wonder of having you. Holding you in my arms for the first time. A bond that can never be broken, no matter where you are." I gently stroke her small hand. There is not much left of her. She has gone so thin. Now and then she lightly groans and squints her eyes, but as time goes on her movements die down. It's as if the pain is slowly leaving her, or, more probably, she is leaving her pain. No pain exists where she is going.

I close my eyes and go through all the lovely moments we had together. I want to do this with her as long as she is still here. Somehow I think I can calm her by sharing this with her, show her the wonderful times she had. Even if much too short, she should see how loved she was and how she loved back. In my mind I go back to our cottage. All is black and white. Bill and I have lost our wrinkles. Sue is small, she is a child again. We are together in our home, playing games on the carpet. Laughing at each other. Bill tries to trick her, but our Sue was always too smart and realises.

Then we are outside. Sue has grown and is becoming a beautiful teenager. We are harvesting vegetables and fruits in our garden. Well, not all of us. Sue is harvesting them straight into her mouth. Blue marks on the side of her lips give away that she has been secretly eating the blackberries. Bill is not very successfully in trying to tell her off. They end up hugging each other, and Sue sneakily winks at me.

Then she is at university. All grown-up and looking smart in her graduation uniform. Throwing her hat in the air with all of her colleagues and Chris. The door to the world stands open to her. Bill and I shed tears of pride watching her.

The children. First she had Matthew in her arms after the difficult birth. The overwhelming glow of the pride of motherhood was all around her. Her angels were coming. Then Kathy and David. They are all the centre of her life. All she ever wanted, all she ever lived for. Having a family of her own and hearing children's voices in her home was her dream come true.

Outside, the sun was sinking behind the lake and the day was coming to an end. A stunning view that made our situation in the hospital room even more surreal.

Sue had gone very calm. There was no more movement. The doctor is with us to examine her. Her pulse is weak and her blood has left her legs. So much I could understand. The doctor goes on explaining something to Chris in German. Chris is nodding and looking down at the ground. He has gone all pale and is fighting his tears. Once the doctor has left, he turns to us to explain. "Sue is very close to going. It won't take long. A nurse will be here in a minute to give her some medication to make the situation more comfortable for her," he explains us in a very controlled manner. "We should say our final goodbyes," he adds, and cannot control himself anymore. Bitterly he cries, and crouches down holding himself. All that he has held together during the day crumbles beneath him. Bill and I stand in shock, trying to digest what he has just told us. After a second, Bill moves over and holds Chris. Blankly we look at each other. Sue is leaving us.

There is a knock at the door. A second later, a nurse quietly opens the door and walks through the room with a small tray. She hardly makes a noise. After placing the tray down on the side table she fills an injection with some transparent fluid. For a second she shyly looks up at us. Then she places the needle and injects the key to heaven into the drip and makes an adjustment to the regulator. Without a sound she places the injection back down on the tray, pauses a second and then looks at us in a sympathetic way. All is calm and feels unreal. Picking up her tray, she turns and leaves the room without looking up at us again.

We sit back down around Sue. She looks so calm. I can only just hear her breath. On the right side of me, I can hear the regular dripping noise of the fluid slowly making its way from the bottle into the tube leading into Sue's lower arm. Her heartbeat is recorded on the monitor next to the bed. The green curve slowly levels out. My girl is leaving us.

Suddenly, Sue takes two deep breaths and peacefully exhales with a light smile on her lips. The sadness around her eyes eases off. Her body sinks even further into the white bedding while her muscles relax. On the monitor, the green curve flattens down to a straight line.

I take a deep breath and slowly exhale. The temperature in the room seems to have sunken. A sudden chill surrounds me, and I believe I can see my breath.

On the other side of the bed, Chris buries his head in the bedding next to Sue's arm. His body jerks up and down a few times before his tears release. Bill and I hold each other and let our tears flow.

We don't have much time to mourn at the hospital. We need to get back home and face the children. They know their mummy is ill, but they do not know the extent. Chris takes over the heart-breaking task. Bill and I stand by him and help catch the children as they fall.

That night, Bill and I lie in bed holding each other. My heart is torn apart. I feel lost and don't know if I should cry or comfort. There is so much pain everywhere. I feel like we are walking on a freshly frozen lake. The layer of ice beneath us is so thin. Just one wrong move and we can fall. Fall into the deep and cold unknown. I can hear the ice moan warning me with every word I try to say. One more word and the icy layer beneath me cracks. Looking down, I see sharp uneven rifts chasing each other across the surface. I freeze. No more movement. No more words.

After what feels like hours of lying in bed trying not to move, I fall into a restless sleep. I am back in the tunnel, but this time it is different. Wind is blowing through the corridor sweeping away the gravel around my feat. The air is dry. The tunnel lightens and I can see the green slippery walls. It looks like the dampness is being sucked out of the moss. Wet drops are popping up to the surface and running away, all in the same direction. As if a giant hoover was sucking up all the dampness. The mosses' colour turns from olive to brown. Dry pieces peel off and fly away down the tunnel until nothing is left. The remaining bare, sand-coloured walls quietly crack. My hands feel dry. Looking down at them, I see a fine layer of dust going all the way up my arms to my shoulders. I clap my hands together and a grey cloud of dust rises, I can see my skin again. It's smooth and white, the way it has always been. The wind slowly dies down and I hear laughter echo off the walls. "There we go. There we go. All is done. All is done," whispers out of the cracks in the walls, followed by dirty laughter. I can see light in front of me, and I quickly walk towards it. Around me, the walls start to crumble, letting even more light and fresh air surround me. The tunnel dissolves. The remaining dust swirls around my feet and rises upwards like a spiral to the sky. I can hear the clapping of birds' wings. The bright light blinds me, and I can only make out a silhouette that is rising to the sky. I quickly shade my eyes to get a better view. I can only make out the movement of something beautiful and bright, something much bigger than life.

I am lying in bed without moving this night. Quiet tears run down my face, fine dry crusts building around my eyes and I murmur to myself "Don't go! Don't go! You are so beautiful!"

Bill, Chris and I go into survival mode. There is so much to do, so much to think about and prepare. A funeral is carried out in Switzerland in the traditional way, followed by a cremation. We believe this is the best way to eliminate the demons that took her. A couple of days later, Chris and the children drive over to England with her ashes. Bill and I are planning a burial in Church Stretton. We feel it is only right to bring our daughter home. She always missed England, and we strongly believe she belongs here.

We discuss the options with Chris. Three people can be buried in one plot. It's given to Bill and me that this would be our family grave. For Sue, Bill and I. Our ashes would be united. But the topic is difficult. How do you explain this to a young husband that has just lost the love of his life?

Our idea doesn't go down well. Chris wants to have the plot for Sue and himself. Our discussion is quickly ended. To digest our disappointment, Bill and I take a walk up the hills.

"We can't expect Chris to allow us to have the plot with Sue. It's too early to be able to talk about that kind of thing," Bill tells me in a dry tone. "I understand all that you are saying. But we have to be realistic. Chris is young. Once his wounds have healed, the chances are high that he will re-marry. I mean look at me. I won't be buried with my first husband Jack. I will be buried with you," I explain. Bill nods. "It upsets me too. But I don't see what we can do. There is too much broken glass on the ground already. We cannot risk any more shattering, especially for the sake of the children. We need to make sure that we maintain a good relationship. We can't risk also losing our grandchildren," Bill kicks some loose soil in frustration. It's rare that such feelings overcome Bill. He is such a calm person. The grief of losing our only child is not the only feeling we are learning to live with. An unexpected, new fear of possibly loosing the contact to our three grandchildren has grown. We do not show our emotions. We do our best to stay calm. But we are torn apart inside. And this time I know my heart will not heal. Burying my only child is not something nature prepares parents for. It is not something that should be. The deep frustration and growing anger costs me a lot to overcome. My wound is septic. Every now and then I feel the urge to cough up the pus. But I hold back and try to escape to a quiet place as quickly as possible. There, I can then let my tears or frustration go.

"Well, I guess we will just need to buy the plot next to Sue for ourselves. This way we will be at least next to each other one day," Bill announces, and I know the discussion is final for him. He can't stand to talk about it anymore. He takes my hand and leads me down the path. "We should get back. I want to make the reservation before it's too late," Bill explains. Together, we walk down the hill to our home.

CHAPTER EIGHTEEN

Two years pass until we see the children in Switzerland again. Matthew is a real teenager now, he is 14 years old and Kathy is close behind him with her 12 years of age. David is eight, and not too interested in what his siblings are up to.

Chris has been very good to us and has kept contact. We both are very grateful for this. Our grandchildren are our only relatives beside Barbara, my brother's daughter. The three of them mean the world to us, and it is quite a shock to find them in a desolate shape. Every one of them seem to be in a world of their own. Occupied in somehow making it work. Ensuring they can survive in any possible way. I don't think this is intentional though. I don't even think that they realize this. I think this just happened due to the unseen pain. We didn't talk about what had happened with Sue. The experience was too hard for us to speak about. Our cowardice and immense pain had taken its toll on the three innocent children. This I'm aware of. But I don't know how to change the situation. I don't want to be a troublemaker. I don't want to stir something up. To be honest, I don't know how to handle the situation myself.

They are with the second English nanny since Sue died. The nannies are young girls that don't really know how to bring up three children. They are more interested in getting to know another country and learn the language. I don't even think they are too bothered with children. The children are more of a burden they have to carry in order to be able to have the experience of being abroad. They seem more occupied with their own situation. But how could you expect anything else from them at their age, and with their lack of experience. At least they were getting lunch and someone was home.

Bill and I do the best we can to help get them all get sorted again. The time we had with them is only a small window. A few opportunities to spend some happy time together and renew our bond. The news that Chris will drop the children off at our home next summer fills us with joy. I cannot wait. For four weeks we will have the children only for ourselves.

Preparing the cottage for a teenager and two children is quite an effort. "I didn't realize that I have so many things," I sigh, piling china into the back room. "Neither did I," Bill chimes in, with a worried smile on his face. "You need to slow down a bit," he warns me. "But look how beautiful," I show him a pinkish bowel with little ladybirds on it. "Yes, definitely," he answers me, a little absent. "Never mind," I tell myself. "I just wonder where I got this from?" I ask myself aloud. I can hear Bill walking back into the landing. There is still a lot more that needs a safe spot. And I need to clear the spare wardrobes upstairs. I have things in there I bought, not because they fit me, but because I just couldn't resist their beauty. "One day they'll fit Kathy. She will love them," I tell myself, thinking of a black velvet jacket with colourful flowers on it that I bought only a week ago in the second-hand shop down the village. "And the money is for a good purpose. They use it to save animals that don't have a home. The poor little dogs and cats," I go on telling myself. Bill is back with some shiny brass pieces, looking at me a little puzzled. "I was just talking to myself. You know, having a little chat," I smirk at him, a little embarrassed. "You taking that medication of yours, are you?" He teases me. A little heat rushes into my face. How dare he! I think to myself. Okay, I have to admit, I have got a little forgetful. But I am getting on. Instead of answering, I just whistle a little tune and we both carry on.

Chris drops the children off as planned. He cannot stay. He has to get back to work and will be back in four weeks time. Three children are quite a handful. By the time they are in bed, Bill and I are shattered, and realize that, at over 70, we are not the youngest grandparents anymore. But we love to have them here.

Bill has prepared a lot of outings, and Kathy goes to the local school with Bethany for the first two weeks. On a Sunday, we decide to go down to the cemetery to look after Sue's grave. We round the children up in the garden to pick pretty flowers. Our garden is bursting and there is a lot of choice. Each of them chooses some flowers. Together, we get quite a bunch together. "There we go. That looks lovely," I tell them. We have a mix of colours and sorts. Sue will love this, I think to myself. The five of us make our way down to the cemetery. It's a good 20-minute walk from our cottage. We walk in silence. It's a strange feeling going there. My tummy always feels a little upset, and I can feel my fear wrenching.

The cemetery lies in a beautiful area. It's off the street down a little lane, with a forest on the one side and an open field with horses grazing on the other. Some large trees shade the stones from the hot summer sun. If you are quiet, you can see the cemetery's inhabitants, little grey rabbits, hopping from one stone to the other. Looking for fresh flowers to eat. On the one hand annoying, but on the other hand I enjoy seeing them. They aren't doing any wrong. They are just taking advantage of the offer of food. And they look so lovely in their little furry suits.

"Matthew, fill the watering can with water over there, will you?" Bill asks him. Matthew runs off, glad to have something to do and not just have to stand in front of Sue's stone. Bill empties his bag of tools. He has brought a brush with him and some gardening scissors. It's our little routine to clean up the grave and place some fresh flowers. The work is needed, and it makes things easier if you have something to do.

David sits down on the path and plays with his shoelaces. Soon Matthew is back with the large watering can filled to the brim. He can hardly carry it. "Okay, now you can pour some water over the stone so we can scrub it," Bill explains. "Don't forget the Bishop," I tell them. A bishop is buried next to Sue's grave. He doesn't seem to have much family. It's clear to see that his stone is not being looked after. We have made it part of our routine to also clean and tidy up his as well. It distracts, gives us something to do and it looks nice if Sue's neighbours are also all in order.

Matthew splashes water all over the stones. Bill hands Kathy the brush. She kneels down next to her mother's stone and starts scrubbing. The view of the two, Kathy scrubbing and Matthew now and then pouring fresh water over the stone breaks my heart. They are so young, and already taking care of their mother's gravestone. I turn and pretend to study some of the other graves while I gather myself. I feel my tummy bubbling. Emotions are pushing up and I have nowhere to hide. Everything has gone so well. I don't want to upset the situation by ripping open wounds that are healing. "Be strong. Be strong!" I tell myself over and over again. "Nana, have you seen that?" David is pulling my hand and is pointing at something. "Look! It's a heart stone," he carries on without looking at me. I follow where his finger is pointing. I swallow hard to under press back the rising salvia. "Yes, it is," I tell him, stroking his hair. Together we walk over to the stone. "It was a young lady. They must have loved her very much," I just manage to stutter, studying the heart-shaped stone. "Nana, are we going back soon?" David asks, looking up at me. I can lose myself in his big brown eyes. They are so deep and full of innocence. "Yes, soon. Lets see how the others are getting on," I smile at him. "You know, I can go up the wood and collect some sticks for the Rayburn. I like doing that," he chatters on, not letting go of my hand. My heart makes a jump and I kiss his head.

Bill is cutting the grass around the stones. "There we go. What do you think?" Bill asks us. "That looks nice. Kathy, do you want to arrange the flowers?" I ask. Quickly she grabs the bunch we picked in our garden and carefully sticks one flower after the other into the gravestone's flowerpot.

Walking back, we all feel lighter. The children are more active and run around in front of us. I feel that we all did well. Bill reaches for my hand, and we comfortably stroll home.

The weeks with the children pass in no time. Bill and I have to admit that we're exhausted. We are definitely getting old, and looking after three children has got a little too much for us.

Chris is back with the car to pick the three up. "How was the drive Chris?" Bill asks him after he has arrived. "Oh you know, it was long and busy. But I had a stopover in Belgium. My brother Jeremy lives there," he tells us. "That's nice. Did he put you up?" Bill carries on, casually asking. "Not this time. A few weeks ago, he introduced me to Marika. We have been seeing each other a few times and I could stay over at her place," he tells us, as if it was the most normal thing of the world. Which I guess it would be. But our situation as Sue's parents is a little different, and this information is a bit too much knowledge for us. Bill turns away from him, and walks to the kitchen as if he needs something. But I know that he doesn't. I can tell from his body language that the information hurts him. He looks stiff, and even though I can't see his face, I know his lips must have turned to a thin line. "Oh, okay," I try to end the conversation. "Tomorrow you are driving to your Mum's, aren't you?" I carry on. "Yes, we will be staying there two nights and then driving back home. I plan to stop in Belgium again for one night. That will make the drive easier," he explains. A shock of horror runs through me. How can he tell us this? Is he planning on staying at this woman's place with the children? I don't dare ask. I feel lost for words. "There is a hotel close to the motorway that I spotted, and isn't too expensive. I think I will stop there for the night. Maybe Marika will join us and I can introduce her," he carries on, as if this is the most normal thing in the world to discuss with us. Bill walks out of the backdoor into the garden. "Just fetching some wood," he murmurs to himself. Trust him, I think. But I know a waterfall of pain is crushing down on him. This is a topic he cannot take. Neither can I, but I'm left no choice. I want to end the conversation. I don't want the last four weeks to finish this way. "Well, it has been a tiring time. We should get some rest. You'll be on the road tomorrow," I tell Chris, while clearing-up the glasses. "I'll just sit a while if you don't mind. I bought a beer down town. I will enjoy that and then go to bed," he says with a smile. "I miss the dark English beer and crisps," he adds with a wink. Bill walks back in through the backdoor. "I just told Chris that we are deadbeat and off to bed," I inform Bill. He nods. "Okay, good night," I wish Chris, before closing the door to the landing.

Upstairs in bed, we both cannot sleep. The new infor- mation troubles us too much. We knew one day this would happen. But it is still a shock to us. "You know it is nice for Chris if he finds someone he likes," I try to soothe the situa- tion, but Bill doesn't answer. "I'm just surprised that he tells us in such an open way. I mean, we aren't his parents. He must realize that this hurts us. The way I understand it, it's early days. They only just got to know each other," I explain, also to myself. Bill just grunts. "We better get some sleep," is all he can reply. We both turn, but none of us falls asleep very quickly this night. Too many thoughts are racing through our mind.

The next day, the car is quickly packed and the children ready to go. "How about Christmas in Switzerland?" Chris asks us before jumping into the driver's seat. Bill and I look at each other. Christmas with the children would be nice I think to myself. "Yes, let us check the flights," I smile. Maybe all is not so bad, I think to myself. "Good, let me know," he cheerfully replies and swings himself into the car. The motor roars and they slowly drive down the lane. The children press their faces to the car windows and wave. We wave back until we cannot see them anymore.

All is quiet back in the cottage. It's empty. As I try to order my mind and go through all I need to do, I inhale deeply. When exhaling I cannot help noticing something new building inside of me. It's a fine layer of anxiety that is comfortably sitting itself down on the corner of my heart. I scold myself and see the anxiety inside of me smiling back.

We arrive in Switzerland two days before Christmas. Chris is busy bouncing back and forth. He is preparing Christmas dinner. A large turkey and all kinds of vegetables to go with it. The children are excited, but somehow very much for themselves. They seem preoccupied by their thoughts. Maybe it is because they are teenagers, as in

Matthews's case, or just on the verge of turning into this confusing age, like Kathy. Or maybe it's something else. The good thing is, that they have got quite attached to their third nanny. A little bit of a troublemaker, as Chris tells us. But the children seem to like her. She is open to hugging them and spending time talking, which is more than the others did, and the closest that they have got to a mother compensation.

Confusingly, the telephone keeps ringing. Chris keeps on jumping to his bedroom to take the calls. It doesn't take much for us to realize that this must be his lady friend, if you can put it this way. She seems very persistent. After a call in his room, Chris comes back into the living room with a smile on his face. "I have offered to let Marika join us. She has been asking to come for days, so I have asked her to join us," he tells us with a bright smile. Bill and I feel smacked in the face. We just sit there and stare into his face. But Chris doesn't seem to realize. He has a hundred things on his mind and immediately rushes to the next. Bill and I just look at each other. I am shocked. Bill is shocked. Chris is back in the kitchen. "Well, looks like we will get to see who she is," I whisper turning to Bill. "She is probably nice," I carry on, trying not to let the atmosphere plunge. Bill just looks at me. "Lets hope she is," he dryly answers. We both lean back and finish our tea.

The next day she arrives. She is a small blonde lady with short cut hair. She seems shy, and doesn't look for much conversation with us. As she is tired from the long train ride, she's off to bed quickly.

We are up early as usual the next day. The flat is quiet, and Bill and I enjoy some time for ourselves. Gradually, one grandchild after the other joins us.

The children sit passively in the flat. They don't mention a thing. But what is there to say, the situation is awkward for all of us. Being witnesses of this newly starting relationship upsets us both, and makes the situation we are in difficult to handle. Bill cannot take it any longer. He stands up and walks to our room and fetches our jackets. "Lets go for a walk. It's not getting any better if we stay here," he tells me while taking my hand. We put on our coats and leave the flat.

The cold winter air pinches our faces, but we don't mind. We need to be out, we need the fresh air. In silence, we walk away from the flat. "I can't understand what is happening. Chris has been so good to us. And now this. I don't know how to handle this," I start. "Sometimes I think he gets us mixed-up, as his friends or maybe parents. But we aren't. We are the parents of his wife who has very sadly died," I carry on, but Bill interrupts me. "It's Christmas! I don't think it is appropriate for us to meet like this for the first time," Bill explains in an upset tone. "We need to stay calm, Bill. We are here to see our grandchildren. That is what it's about. We need to understand that he needs to carry on with his life too, and I won't risk losing our contact to the three children," I explain. "Well, coming to Switzerland again isn't an option for me," Bill tells me in a serious tone. "The children are nearly old enough. They will be able to fly to England by themselves soon, and we can organize to get them picked-up at the airport," he tells me without looking at me. I know he is serious about it. We take a few deep breaths before turning back. We know we have two more days to get through.

Back in England, we hear that things are going quickly with Chris and Marika. She has moved in and the nanny has had to leave after some commotion with Chris. Now the children spend a lot of time at a day mother's house.

The information worries and upsets us both. But we don't know what to do. We are afraid of losing contact if we are too harsh on Chris. On the other hand, we feel we need to step in to a certain degree, especially for our daughter who would not want to see her children being pushed aside and neglected. It is like balancing on a high wire, and not know-ing if there is a safety net beneath us.

CHAPTER NINETEEN

I am caught in what feels like a small room. I don't know where I am. All the walls seem very close and the air is thick and hot. It's dark and my eyes only gradually adjust. Carefully, I make one step forward, stretching my arms out in front of me. The ground beneath my feet is slippery, as if I am walking on a carpet of slimy seaweed. A foul smell surrounds me. "Careful, careful," the room whispers to me. Startled I look around, but all is pitch black. I take another step forward, carefully keeping my balance. My outstretched arm touches something soft. It feels like a damp sponge. Cool fluid runs between my fingernails and down my lower arm to my elbow and starts dripping onto the ground. I quickly pull my arm back and try to wipe away the liquid. But it has already dried, and there is only a sticky crust left that starts to itch my skin. "We are quick! We are quick this time," the room whispers to me. "What is going on? Where am I?" I ask myself. The skin on my arm starts to feel like it's burning. "We can hear you, Mollie. Even if you don't speak aloud, we hear you," a familiar long dirty laugh follows. In shock, I stand and squeeze my eyes closed. "Just wake up. Just wake up!" I tell myself again and again. I just want to be out of wherever I am. I'm afraid and I don't understand why I am back with these creatures. They had gone, I saw them dry out and turn to dust. They were blown away by the wind. My body shakes in fear and I feel my foot slip. I quickly balance myself by touching the spongy substance on the wall in front of me. Once again cool liquid runs down my arm, this time all the way to my shoulder. The fluid tickles like carbonic acid and dries quickly, leaving my skin feeling like it is burning. As if I had fallen into a bush of stinging nettles. "Do you admire our quick work?" A husky voice asks me from the corner of the room. "We are quick this time. Quick. Quick. Quick!" Other voices whisper. "I don't understand," is all I manage to say. "You always want to understand. But there is nothing to understand. This is what we are. This is what we are here for," the voice hisses. The stale smell of its breath makes me feel faint. Everything is turning around me. First slowly, and then always faster, followed by a chorus of dirty laughter.

I wake up feeling sick. Quickly I jump out of bed and run to the bathroom.

After coming back to bed, I lie awake for a while. Next to me, I hear Bill moan in his sleep. He seems to have pain. He has had this for some time now in the stomach area. We thought that he had maybe just eaten something bad that wasn't digesting well, and Bill never admits to feeling that something is wrong with his body. Luckily, we have finally made an appointment with our doctor for tomorrow, I think to myself while turning to one side.

The next day, Bill is thoroughly examined by our doctor. This takes some time, and I'm left in the waiting room. The assistant hands me a form to fill in. They need an update of Bill's data. Carefully I go through each question. First I need to fill in the usual information, such as full name, address, date of birth and so on. Strangely, I get stuck with some questions. Not that I don't understand them. I even know the answer, but I just cannot get it out of myself. It feels like they are stuck somewhere between my brain and my fingers that are holding the pen. A little confused, I sit there and go through them again and again, and use my fingers to try and help me count. But I just cannot get it out. "This is silly. What is Bill's date of birth?" I ask myself sharply. There is a knock on the door, and the assistant is back. "Mollie, they're finished with the check-up. Would you like to join them for the results?" She asks me kindly, and reaches for the forms she gave me. "Oh yes, of course, I will join them," I pause, because I know I haven't filled in all the required information. The assistant stands there without moving, waiting for me to pass her back the paper. "Err, I haven't managed to fill in all you are asking for," I mutter. "Don't worry, let me see," she steps towards me and takes the paper, without waiting for me to reply. She scans the document and then looks back at me a little puzzled. I don't know what to say, but I know I have left too many questions open. "Well, let's go through to the doctor's office. He can collect the missing pieces from Bill," she smiles gently at me, and shows me the way. A little embarrassed, I follow her. Hopefully I've got out of this, I think to myself. This has been happening quite often lately, I go on thinking.

The assistant opens the door to a bright office with a dark brown desk and two chairs on the visitor's side of the table. All is very clean and neat. There are some dummy body pieces standing on the corner of the table that can be used to demonstrate. It all looks very sophisticated. I sit down and rest my handbag on my knees. On the other side of the room, the door opens and the doctor walks in, followed by Bill. Both look very serious. Bill is looking down to the ground while he walks over to me and sits down on the free chair next to me. "Mollie, nice to see you," the doctor stretches out his arm to shake my hand. "How are you doing?" He asks me. "Oh, I am okay, thank you," I reply. "You had some problems with some of the questions?" He asks me, pointing to the forms. I nod, feeling a little silly. "Let me see," he scans the paper. "Date and place of birth?" He asks. Bill looks at me a little puzzled while answering. "I had them on the tip of my tongue, I just couldn't get them out," I defend myself, feeling my cheeks going all pink. "Well, that happens sometimes, doesn't it," the doctor replies with a sincere smile on his face. "But it's been happening quite a lot lately," Bill gives me away with a worried look on his face. How dare he tell, I think to myself. We aren't here because of me!

"And collecting things. You don't even remember that you do it," Bill carries on. I look at him with widened eyes, trying to tell him to stop. But he ignores me and concentrates on the doctor. "Um," the doctor thinks for a while. "It's probably best if we run some tests. It won't hurt. You know, just to be sure everything is okay. What do you think, Mollie?" He asks me. "I will get Alison to make you an appointment," he carries on, without waiting for me to reply. I just swallow and nod. I want this discussion to be ended.

"Mollie, we have run some tests on Bill. The pain in his lower stomach area is unfortunately serious. His blood values are not showing good results. I'm afraid we think we have found prostate cancer indications. To be sure, and to be able to determine the stage, I'm organizing a thorough medical check at Shrewsbury Hospital," he explains. Sitting in my chair, I believe myself to be in a surreal scene. "No, this is not me! This is not Bill! No, we have carried our part of cancer, we have paid our dues. This is not us! This is a mistake!" goes through my mind. I just sit and try to order my thoughts. "Mollie, if we act quickly the chances are good that Bill can be successfully treated. But we must wait for the experts to examine him at the hospital," the doctor tries to calm the situation. I fiddle with the strap of my handbag. "How could this happen," I finally blankly ask. "If it is what we assume, prostate gland cancer, there are several treatment possibilities. Unfortunately it has become quite a widely spread form of cancer with men. Especially at your age, I'm afraid," the doctor explains, with a serious expression on his face. I feel Bill take my hand. "It will be okay, dear. We just need to make sure you get my data right. I guess we will be filling out a lot of forms," he smiles at me, full of love. "I need you to be fit," he tells me. I swallow hard. "Trust you to turn the situation on me," I tell him with a broken voice. Tears are pooling in my eyes but I want to be strong. I must be strong for Bill.

The hospital results confirm our doctor's assumption. Bill has an advanced stage of prostate cancer. The plague is back in our family, and this time we didn't notice it coming. Bill is in and out of the hospital, but the therapy is not providing the needed results. Bill quickly decided for himself that he doesn't want to go anymore. He wants to spend his time at home. This is where he most wants to be, this is where he finds his peace.

"Mollie, are you back?" I hear Bill call me from the bedroom. I close our front door quietly. I actually didn't want to wake him up. I know his medication makes him tired and he needs regular rests during the day. "Yes, I am here. I will just be up," I confirm. I place my handbag down near the cloakroom and hang up my jacket. Everything as usual, everything the way it needs to be. "See, I can do that! And I will find you all again," I tell myself, my jacket and my handbag, with a sad smile on my face. Walking into the living room I wonder what I actually wanted to do in here. "Er, that is annoying, what did I want to do?" I ask myself. "Oh, the post. Where did I put it? Okay, go through all your steps again and you will find it," I tell myself. I start off again at the door. "Ah, here it is," I speak out aloud. "What is where?" Bill shouts down. "The post, I was looking for the post," I reply and walk into the living room.

While I wait for the kettle to heat the water, I go through the post, nothing really significant. I prepare two cups. My mind goes back to my handbag. "Yes, yes I know. They won't hurt, they will make everything easier," I tell myself, and walk back to the landing. And there they are inside my handbag, two neat bottles with white pills inside them. I fetch them out and walk back into the living room. "One each every day," I repeat what the doctor told me. "See, not that bad, I can remember that." I smile to myself, and pop two pills into my mouth and swallow them down with some water.

I walk upstairs to see Bill with two cups of tea. He is lying in bed and staring up at the ceiling. He has lost some weight and muscle, that I cannot deny. "Here you go, some fresh tea," I tell him, placing the two cups down. "Thank you. So how did it go? What did the doctor say?" He asks me. Sitting on the side of the bed, I look down to my fingers, feeling a little nervous and start sliding my wedding ring up and down my finger. "Well, as we thought, I am getting a little forgetful," I smile. "So?" Bill asks. "It's difficult to make a clear diagnosis in such cases. But it could be dementia," I swallow. Bill takes my hand and kisses the back of it. "I guess I just don't want to remember everything," I try to chuckle. "He has given me some medication to slow things down, so things don't get worse," I add. "Don't worry, Mollie. We are getting old. That is the way it is. I am glad you went and got some help," he tells me with a proud tone. "We need to be realistic and get some things sorted. We got to talk about what will happen," he tells me looking deep into my eyes. After all these years I can still get lost in his eyes. His heart is so good and full of love. He is my second part, and there hasn't been one day that we haven't spent together. A hard lump has built in my throat. Even though I try to swallow it down, I cannot stop it rising again. I don't want to talk about it, I think to myself, but Bill doesn't let me go, he wants to talk. Tears build and I have no choice than to let them roll down. Bill pulls me close into his embrace. We lie together on our bed and I cry bitter tears.

I don't know how long we stay like that and it doesn't matter. I enjoy every moment of feeling his warmth around me. Gently he strokes my hair and kisses my head. "I was thinking of Barbara," he calmly whispers. "She is so good. She is a bit like a daughter to us. I think she would be a good choice," he tells me. "What do you mean?" I ask with a thin voice. "She could be our guardian. You know, be the one that takes decisions for us if we become to weak and forgetful," he explains. I raise my head and look into his eyes. "Mollie, I think my time is running out. I feel I am leaving soon. I want to be sure all is sorted and that you have help," he explains with tears in his eyes. "I want to go knowing you are looked after. That will make it easier for me. I love you so much, and I know one day we all will be together again. But until then we have to make sure you have all that's needed," he goes on. "Don't say that," I beg him. He smiles at me and strokes my hair. He looks tired and weak. "Barbara," I repeat. "Barbara is a good choice," I confirm. Bill relaxes back into his cushion. "That's good," he smiles looking relieved. "Now, let's have that cup of tea," he winks at me and I pass him his cup.

Barbara and her husband George are angels. They immediately agree to be our guardians. It doesn't take long for a legal attorney to set up a document that we all sign. At the same time, we also decide to draw up our last will. It seems right for us to do this. We want to be sure that our grandchildren will one day be our only heirs, never matter what happens.

The settling of our situation is the needed peace for Bill. His health quickly worsens, and he soon can hardly leave the bed. A nurse and doctor come to check his situation daily and help me wash him. It's Bill's deepest wish not to go to hospital. He wants to spend his last days at home where he feels most comfortable, where we can be together.

The news that Chris and Marika have married just passes us by. Not that our thoughts are not with the family, and especially with our grandchildren. But we are just to caught-up with Bill's new path, and consequently mine.

After dinner in bed, we sit together and I read Bill the newspaper. "So, let's hear what's going on in the world," Bill whispers. He can hardly keep his eyes open. His face is torn with pain. "I will fetch you your medication. You don't look too good," I tell him, and stroke his hair out of his face. Bill grunts. "That would be nice," he smiles and for a short moment opens his eyes and looks at me.

I don't need to go far, I have sorted all his medication on my dressing table. "Here you go." I place the little white pill into his mouth and carefully support his head so he can swallow it down with some water. "That's better," he sighs and sinks back down into his pillow.

We lay together and I read him some local stories while he nods off. He looks peaceful and happy, at peace with the world and himself. I put the newspaper down and lay facing him. He tries to murmur something, but cannot get the words out right. Gently I stroke his forehead, and slide a little closer to him. "I love you Mollie! I will be waiting for you with our girl. You know that," he manages, and a single tear runs down the side of his face. Inside, my heart is close to breaking. I don't want to break the peaceful moment though, and desperately fight against the building pressure. Bill peacefully sighs and sinks deeper down into this pillow.

His facial muscles relax and I feel a cool gush of air pass by. All is calm. All is quite. My tummy trembles up and down. I crawl into his arms and press myself against his still warm body as if I want to suck-up every little piece of him before all is gone. I wrap his arm around me and hug my knees. Like a little ball, I lie in his embrace and try to calm my ragged breathing. I don't want to move. I don't want to let go, because when I do, reality will crash in and I am terrified of what stands in front of me. I squeeze my eyes closed and let my tears dry on the pillow. In my mind I can hear the echoing of dirty laughter. The creatures from my dreams are swirling around and around. "All is done, all is done. Here we go, here we go." I hear whispering from all sides, followed by triumphant laughter. In front of me I can see a field of olive green slowly turning dark. It's like watching fruit shrivel and decay within seconds. The grey dust that remains is picked up by a gush of wind that scatters it across the land.

All is gone and I am alone. The wind dies down and all goes dark. The temperature drastically drops and my body begins to tremble. In front of me, a black, windy road is the only path I can take. As the temperature further falls, I can see little crystals quickly gathering across the road in front of me. It looks like they are running to each other and linking their little arms. Within no time, the ground beneath my feet and in front of me has become a sheer sheet of ice. Carefully I take a few steps and balance myself with outstretched arms. In the distance I can hear the wind picking-up again and howling down the windy street. There is nowhere I can go, no place to hide and no shelter. Snowflakes dance in perfect synchrony just above the surface in front of me. Elegantly, they swirl into the air and let themselves drop back down to the ground, only to repeat their enchanting chorography and with every new cycle they get closer to me. The first snowflakes that reach me gently blow across my feet. But the wind picks up quickly and the following ones ruthlessly blow into my face, cutting my skin without mercy.

Alone I stand and watch an icy cold sandstorm of freezing white powder drift across the street, ready to hit me and cut my skin. It knows no friends and it knows no enemies. It only does what it is and leaves without a trace.

CHAPTER TWENTY

Bill's funeral almost passed by without me realizing. It's as if it was just a film I was watching without really being part of. I had so much to organize that I didn't have time to think. Barbara and George helped me wherever they could, I am so grateful. Chris and the grandchildren came over, but had to leave soon again as they had to get back to school.

Back in the cottage all is quiet, too quiet. I am trying not to talk to myself too much because I feel I could be going crazy if I did. I don't want to build-up fantasy figures, I think that would be odd. But now and then I can't stop it and I complain to myself.

"Damn pills, getting stuck in my throat like that. How dare you!" I shout to the white elegant bottle. "I don't know why I'm taking you. I'm fine, just fine," I carelessly push the two white bottles out of my way on the kitchen counter and storm out of the room. Standing in the parlour, I'm unsure. Am I going upstairs, into the sitting room or out? I feel a little puzzled. "What am I doing?" I ask myself. "Okay, okay, don't worry. This is just because I got a little upset getting a nasty-tasting pill stuck in my throat like that," I carry on.

"Bill? Love?" I shout up the stairs. There's no answer. All is quiet, too quiet.

It takes me a couple of seconds to realize what I was originally up to. Looking towards the front door, I see a cotton bag hanging on the door knob. Some pretty flowers are sticking their heads out at the top. "Oh, yes, I'm going to the cemetery. Silly me, how could I forget," I scold myself. Since Sue's passing away it has been a routine to walk down to the graveyard once a week. Make sure everything is in order and that there are some fresh flowers decorating the stone.

"Right, my coat and my shoes, that's what I need," I go on, chatting to myself while opening the cloakroom. A couple of minutes later I'm out on the street with my prepared bag. It's a good 20 minutes walk to the cemetery. Walking down the street, I remember thinking to myself that I should be careful about talking to myself. "Gosh, I'm doing it all the time," I tell myself. "Well, Mollie, you are a chatty person. That's what you are!" Another voice in my mind tells me. "Hmm, that's right, I am," I agree. "We will just have to be a bit careful about it," I carry on, thinking.

"Oh, look at those beautiful flowers," I call to myself while passing a small house with garden. "I love those colours!"

I reach the lane that leads down to the cemetery. In a couple of minutes I will have reached my destination. My tummy flips and I feel a slight sickness building inside of me. I feel nervous and fidgety, and I pass my bag back and forth between my hands. Whatever I do I cannot make myself feel comfortable. I open the gate and turn right to where Sue's stone lies. The small path is being attacked from both sides by trailing weeds. The sun is shining through the trees that shade the stones, and, every now and then, bright rays of sunlight touch me, warming my body. "Here we are," I tell myself, reaching Sue's stone. For a moment I stand still and read the engraving. Something is different. Next to Sue's stone there is an almost identical new stone. I start to read the engraving. The first word already brings me back to reality. "Bill," I think to myself, and absently wipe my eyes with a tissue. For a few more seconds I stand and wait, while all that has happened crashes over me like a giant wave. Inside, an immense strength is preventing me from breaking down. My small family lies in front of me, and I realize that all I want is to be able to be with them. Reunited, somewhere else. "If I could just hold you both in my arms," I inwardly cry to myself, feeling the deepest pain rip my heart apart. Dabbing my eyes, I order myself to fetch the watering can. At least I can clean up their stones, everyone shall see how loved they are.

After pouring some water over the stones, I kneel down and fetch a gardening brush out of my bag. I brush the stones and the gold engraving. "There you go, that looks better," I tell them. The little water I have left I pour over the bishop's grave next to them and give him a little scrub too. Looking after his grave is part of the procedure. It always has been.

I carefully sort the flowers. The pinkish colours for Sue and the yellow ones for Bill. Back on my feet, I gaze back down on my work. "Well, I guess it's time to get back," my inner voice tells me. I look up at the sky through the branches of the tree. The sun has gone and I feel a little chilly. I gather my equipment together and place it back in my cotton bag. Walking back, I feel heavier than when I came. Reality seems to have laid weights on my shoulders, and my sadness is pressing on my heart.

All is quiet at home, and I am all alone. A small cooked dinner and the television warm me a little. Tomorrow is shopping day, I remind myself. This cheers me up a little - I will have a real person to talk to. Nancy, my neighbour, and I have made it a weekly routine that we go down the town together to buy the necessaries and to treat ourselves to a tea or coffee in one of the local teahouses. "I better get my shopping list ready," I tell myself. But I feel too heavy to move, I just want to sit for a while. If a small wave of energy reaches me I will make it upstairs to bed. So I sit and wait for it to happen.

The next day I'm up early. Lying in bed with my eyes open, I wish I could sleep longer. It would make the day shorter if I could manage to sleep a little longer. I wouldn't have so many hours of thinking what I should do. I turn to one side and study my alarm clock. It's 7:45 a.m. I watch the clock's second hand go round and round again. Minutes pass, but nothing happens. There are no sounds in the house. All is quiet, too quiet. This puzzles me. "There used to be more sound, I'm sure," I tell myself. My alarm clock tells me it's 7:50. I turn back onto my back and stare up at the ceiling. Lying very calmly, I can just hear my alarm clock counting the seconds. Tick-tack, tick-tack, it whispers. My eyes follow a faint crack in the ceiling. Tick-tack, tick-tack. Now that I have noticed the ticking sound, I can't fade it out anymore.

I study the crack in the ceiling a little longer. At one end it breaks into three tiny little openings. If I were to follow the cracks with a black felt-tip it would look like a skinny arm with three fingers. "How pointless is this observation," I grumble. My alarm clock reads 7:56. "I really should get up," I tell myself. "Just a few more seconds," the lazy-me pleads, and I obey by relaxing my muscles once more. "So, let's go through the day. What do I want to do?" I ask myself. "Oh, Nancy, yes of course, we are going down the town. I should make a list," I think. The thought makes me feel I have something to do. Suddenly, I feel I have a purpose. I quickly get up and walk into the bathroom for a wash. The church bells strike eight times outside . Inside the cottage, all remains quiet, too quiet.

A week later, Barbara, my brother's daughter, is coming over to visit me. The night before I had a telephone call with Chris. Kathy, my granddaughter, will be over to visit in a few weeks time. I am excited to have company, and happy to have some real news to tell Barbara.

A knock on the door makes me jump out of my thoughts. Looking through the living room window I can see Barbara and George waiting at the front door. I quickly let them in, and enjoy the moment of embrace. "How are you, Mollie," Barbara asks me carefully, studying my face. "Oh, I am fine, you know, just the usual," I explain, taking their coats to the cloakroom. I want to spare my news for later on. "That can't be right," I hear George say. He is inspecting his wristwatch and looking back to Bill's grandfather clock standing in the parlour. "The grandfather needs winding-up, Mollie," he tells me, still studying his wristwatch. "Does it? Bill always does….," I stop myself in the middle of my sentence. Barbara is looking at me with a sympathetic look on her face. "Let me do that for you," George kindly offers. "I will check the other clocks too. You have quite a collection," he adds with a caring smile. Barbara stretches out her arm and lays it across my shoulders. "I could do with a cup of tea," she smiles and guides me to the living room.

While George winds up all the clocks, Barbara and I make tea and chat. The cottage seems to slowly come back to life again. Tick-tack, tick-tack sounds from everywhere. It is no longer quiet in the cottage. Life is back again.

"How is your medication going?" Barbara asks me while taking a biscuit. "I don't know why I'm taking it. I'm fine, nothing's wrong, I don't understand the fuss," I explain, feeling a wave of frustration rising and colouring my cheeks. "Nothing is wrong, it's a precaution to make sure you're alright. Bill was worried and wanted the best, that's all," she tries to soothe me. "Well, I'm taking them, even though I don't feel any difference. Not that there is a difference to be expected because, as I said, nothing is wrong." This discussion is making me angry. I can feel it and I think I nearly got caught with my last words. "You're right and that's the point. The medication helps to preserve the situation, you're doing wonderfully," she beams at me. A little annoyed, I look around. Where is George sneaking around, I think to myself. "George's tea is getting cold," I try to casually mention. "He will be here any minute, I'm sure," Barbara nonchalantly replies. "You do have a lot of clocks, you know," she adds. I feel uncomfortable and caught in my seat. The backdoor opens and in comes George. "Are there clocks out there too? Where are you coming from?" I ask, a little harshly. "All your clocks are ticking again. I was just round the house, you know, I love your garden," he smiles. I feel that I'm being checked on. "Lovely, some tea," George grabs a cup and flops down next to us. Barbara starts telling me some stories about her sons, but I don't really listen. I'm occupied inwardly scolding them both. I know they're checking on me.

After we've all drunk our tea, Barbara becomes fidgety. "George, what do you think? We should be off soon. I'd like to be home before it gets dark," she orders. "What do you think, Mollie, afternoon tea in two weeks?" she asks with a smile. "Kathy will be over then for a week. I guess I'll be quite busy," I tell her. "Oh, that's lovely. That will be nice for you! Well, then, let's see us again in one month's time." Saying that, she stands up and reaches for her handbag. George follows her and we say our goodbyes.

Once again I'm back alone in the cottage. But this time it is not so lonely. My clocks are ticking and comforting me. It's not so quiet anymore. "Wind up the clocks, wind up the clocks," I repeat in my mind. This is now my task. A routine that I can hold on to, and something to do that will keep me busy. "I'm not going to have George poking around again," I think to myself.

I've noted Kathy's arrival date in the calendar I have hanging close to the kitchen. The days that have already passed are crossed through. This way I always know where I stand. Only now and then I get a little confused about whether I've already crossed off the days or not. In those situations, my daily newspaper helps me find the answer and get everything straight again. Two more days and then she will arrive, which means I'd better start getting things ready. She isn't a child anymore, so I don't have to be too protective of all my valuables. But there again, I don't want her to be shocked. I do have a lot of things everywhere. Wandering through the cottage, I decide to make a mental list of what needs to be stored into the backroom. "Oh, aren't you beautiful," I romanticize, picking up a white bowl with blue painting on it. "Now, where are you from?" I try to remember where I got it from, but it doesn't come to my mind. "Never mind, never mind, it's wonderful to have you here. I will leave you just where you are. Happily, I go on marvelling at all my belongings. My mood is light and I'm feeling energized and happy. After I have finished my tour in the sitting room, I go back to the kitchen. "Now, what was I doing?" I ask myself. I spot my calendar on the other side of the room and decide to take a look; I probably need to cross off another day. Monday, Tuesday and Wednesday have already got a large black X over them. "What day is it today," I ask aloud. "Is it Thursday or Friday? Well it's definitely a weekday, as milk was delivered this morning. Where is the newspaper?" I go on asking myself. "Oh, over there. Now let's see," I pick up the newspaper and scan the front page. "Thursday! There you go," I confirm to myself, and turn back to the calendar. "Oh, well, I have already crossed off Wednesday, so all is in order. My index finger follows across the coming days and I read my notes. "Kathy, arriving on Friday afternoon. Hmm, I should get the house ready," I think. Hesitating a little, I have to kick myself to move. I just don't feel like piling pieces into the backroom. But I should, I don't want her to be shocked, and so I decide to start in the sitting room. Wandering around the room, a white bowl with blue painting catches my eye. "I was just looking at you!" I tell the bowl, while clarity hits me. "Oh gosh, look at me now getting all distracted by a pretty bowl and forgetting what I was here for." I tell myself off. "I need to take those pills! I'm not allowed to forget! I'd better go and take them now," I decide, and walk back into the kitchen to take my medication.

Later on that day, I do actually manage to clear some pieces away and make space for my granddaughter. I think I was avoiding the situation, because I just don't enjoy it. It has nothing to do with my mind. But in any case, I won't risk it, and will keep on taking my daily medication.

CHAPTER TWENTY-ONE

Two days later there's a knock at the door. "Who's that?" I wonder to myself. Just as I finish speaking, the thought hits me like lightning. "Kathy, of course, it's Friday!" I quickly dash to the front door and there she is, all smiley with her beautiful, long red hair. We immediately hug each other and she gives me a big kiss on my cheek. She has grown so tall, at least in comparison to myself.

"Which will be my room, Nana?" She asks me. "You can have Sue's room. I've made the bed ready for you," I smile at her, and she seems very pleased. With her suitcase in her hand, she runs upstairs and I wish I'd cleared a little more from the stairs. Some of the pieces that decorate the sides of the staircase bounce with every step she takes. I follow her up and show her where she can store her clothes. Sue's room is the largest and brightest room. It's a beautiful place to stay. From the window you can look up to the hills. We kept the room in a yellow colour that makes it look even sunnier. There is a dressing table with a matching round mirror on one side of the room. Kathy quickly unpacks her few beauty accessories and lines them up on the dressing table. She looks very proud, which warms my whole body, I enjoy seeing her happy. "How about a drink? You must be thirsty," I ask her. "Yes please," she beams at me, and follows me downstairs. In the kitchen, I fetch the orange squash that I specially bought for her and make myself a cup of black tea. Together, we relax in the armchairs next to the Rayburn. It's nice to have family in the house, and I feel at peace. I am needed, I have tasks, I have a teenager to look after. Feeling full of energy, I lean back and listen to her stories. Watching her, I cannot help thinking of Sue. She is so alike, her green eyes and her full hair. It's like my daughter is back and I'm much younger again. My forgetfulness is gone and far away. I'm full of thoughts and ideas, duties to take care of and things to do.

Over the next days, we spend a lot of time at home and down the village. The little car that Bill and I had has been sold. I never felt comfortable driving. That was always Bill's task and I could sit next to him and look at all the beautiful homes and gardens that we passed by on our journeys. Shortly after he left me, I sadly decided to sell our four wheels. I miss our outings, and wish I could offer a bit more to my granddaughter. But she doesn't seem unhappy, she likes Church Stretton and is off up the woods with the neighbour's dog every day. In the evenings, we stay up after dinner and chat about our lives. It's not easy for her over in Switzerland. The new situation came so quickly. Suddenly she has a stepmother. It's all is very confusing for her and I don't really know what to say. I understand her point of view and I wish I could do something to help. But I am so far away and I don't really know what would help. I am glad that Chris and I have kept up the good relationship, even though I don't agree with all that has happened or is going on. I feel blessed that he still thinks of me and takes care of so many things. If only the situation was easier.

As the days go by with my granddaughter, my good condition of mind astonishes me. I'm up early in the mornings. I don't lie in bed counting the ticks of my alarm clock. No, normally I'm awake before it even rings. By the time Kathy is up, I have the breakfast ready, have done a wash and am already sorting out what we will have for dinner. I don't even have to cross off the days on the calendar. I know which day it is, and feel I have overcome my short, down period of forgetfulness. "I will have to tell Barbara," I proudly say to myself, preparing the breakfast dishes in the kitchen. In the corner of my eye, I can see the two white bottles of pills standing, waiting for me to realize their presence. Happily, I walk over to them and open their lids. They are almost empty. Only a few pills left in each bottle. "Well, I won't be wasteful about them," I tell myself and take one each and swallow them down with the remainder of my tea. "Good morning, Nana," Kathy cheerfully greets me. I jump and only just manage to keep my tea and pills going down the right way. After a cough I greet her back. "You took me by surprise," I smile at her. "What are you taking, Nana?" She asks me, looking at the one white bottle that is still in my hand. A sudden heat rush colours my cheeks. "This?" I ask, trying to win time. She just blinks at me and waits for my answer. "It's this medication they put me on. So that I stay fit and stuff. I've nearly finished the bottle and I think I don't need them anymore," I smile, feeling cheerful. Yes, I don't need them anymore, I think to myself. "Oh, okay, well vitamins are always good to take. What's for breakfast?"

she asks, and inspects the kitchen counter. Quickly I put the white bottle back to its place on the dresser and join her, feeling happy to change the topic. "Dad is arriving tonight, isn't he?" Kathy asks me while fishing out a Weetabix and laying it in her cereal bowl. Nonchalantly I peek over to my calendar. What's today? Thursday, yes it must be Thursday. In large letters I have Chris written on the Thursday's square. "Yes, he is. We'd better go down to the market and buy something for dinner for all of us," I proudly confirm. Everything is in order, I'm getting it all right, I think to myself.

Chris arrives in the early evening. He is all bubbly and full of stories, bouncing from one place to the other and touching all my things. Somehow I cannot help myself thinking that he is somehow inspecting me. He is looking at everything, especially my piles of paper on the dresser. "Oh dear, Mollie, you need to get this one paid! This is a final reminder, if you don't pay within the next ten days they will turn off your electricity," he reads to me, looking a little worried at the letter. What is he talking about! Of course they won't turn off my electricity, I think. Why is he rummaging in my post anyway? "Show me that! Of course I've paid my bills. Pass me my payment booklet that's lying there, will you," I order. Page for page, I go through my paid bills and, indeed, I haven't made an electricity payment for over six months. "I must have missed that one," I admit. "I will get that done on Monday," I ensure them. Chris watches me carefully before turning back to the remaining pile of letters. I wish he would stop. Something catches his eye, and he lays down the pile and takes one of the white bottles and studies the label on the front. Good God, not this too, I think to myself, and quickly close my eyes. "Is this the medication against dementia that you are taking," he asks bluntly. I'm used to Chris speaking his mind, but how dare he say that word to me. The tablets are only a precaution. I do not have dementia! "I don't know what you are talking about. After Bill's death I was a little mixed up. The tablets are to keep me fit and anyway, they'll soon be finished." Ha, now I've put him in his place! I smile to myself. Chris doesn't seem impressed though. He shakes the bottle and puts it back onto the dresser shelf. "Yes, best is if you get an appointment with the doctor so you don't run out. I'm sure Barbara will accompany you," he tells me, and sits down next to me. That was not what I was thinking about, but I keep this thought to myself. I'd prefer to end the discussion.

Later that night, I lie in bed and look at my skinny arm crack on the ceiling. How dare they inspect me like this. This is my home and I'm fine! I turn to one side and eventually fall asleep. Entering my dream world feels like I'm footlessly moving through soft pink candyfloss clouds. The most beautiful melodies are played on harps and I close my eyes to fully take in every tune. Leaning back with my eyes closed, I am pillowed by the softest feathers. I am sheltered and feel warm and safe. Little fine voices great and tease me. It's as if fairies are speaking to me and I open my eyes to see these wonderful creatures but I can't quite make them out. Their little hands are stroking across the pink texture around me. It looks like their long slim fingers are combing candyfloss hair. A sweet scent is in the air and I can taste the most delicious sugar on my lips. The little figures gather together and sing touching songs that awaken childhood memories. Suddenly they are all around me, and are hooking their little arms into mine. We are gently swaying from one side to the other and walking down memory lane together. It's such a wonderful place and I'm tempted to get lost in it. With a smile on my face, I turn to my other side and lick my lips. The taste is heavenly.

My two white bottles have filled again. Barbara made sure I visited the doctor shortly after Kathy and Chris had left. I can't help thinking that Barbara and Chris are in contact. Probably plotting the next steps together. But okay, if taking the pills means they will leave me alone, then I'm prepared to do that. My new candyfloss dreams are making it harder and harder for me to get up in the morning. They are enchanting, and take me away to a safe and beautiful place. On some days I don't see the point of getting up and leaving them.

So it is this morning. I'm lying in bed and just testing out what it feels like to cuddle up on the other side when there is a knock at the door. "Who could that be?" I say to myself. I decide if I stay very quiet they may just go away. Pretend nobody is here, I go on thinking, and smile to myself. But there it goes again, another loud knock that I cannot ignore. Gut wrenching, I stand up and put on my dressing gown. "Who on earth could this be? Did I miss something on my calendar?" I ask myself. A young lady is standing in front of my door . Her dark hair is neatly combed into a ponytail and she is wearing a bright apron kind of dress over jeans.

"Hi, I'm Helen. Are you Mollie?" She asks me with dazzling eyes. I feel embarrassed, my hair must be all over the place. "Um, yes I am. How can I help you?" I ask. "I'm here to clean your house. Don't you remember, Barbara called me for you, I will be here every Wednesday morning for two hours," she brightly smiles, showing off her white teeth. "Oh, did she now. I don't need any cleaning, I am perfectly capable of doing my housework," I reply, making myself tall. "I'm sure you are, but as I'm already here I might as well make myself useful." And saying this, she gently pushes herself through the door. I have no choice but to let her in. "I'll make a start in the kitchen. That will give you some space for yourself upstairs," she explains, vanishing into the living room. "How dare she," I say to myself. On the one hand I feel embarrassed to be standing in my dressing gown close to lunchtime. On the other hand, I feel angry to have some stranger take over my home. Not really having another choice, I go upstairs to get myself washed and dressed. "I will have to highlight the Wednesdays on my calendar," I tell myself, getting my skirt straight. While looking for a matching pearl necklace, I try to go through my last discussions with Barbara. I just cannot remember talking about getting housework help. "I will have to ask her. Or did she just decide by herself that my home is dirty and something had to be done?" I wonder, with an angry wrinkle growing on my forehead. Downstairs, I can hear the Hoover howling up and decide I'd better check what is going on.

After Helen has left, I mark all the Wednesdays with a red colour. "I am not having her catch me in my pyjamas again," I grumble to myself. "And what about my hair?" I go on looking at myself in the mirror. With my fingers, I try to comb my hair into shape what doesn't really work. "I guess I could do with a new perm," I decide, and pick up the phone and call my hairdresser.

A week later, when Helen is back, I feel in much better shape. I'm up in time and my hair is set nicely. I put on a pretty skirt with matching clean top and cardigan. I enjoy a moment of going through all of my pearl necklaces looking for the matching piece. "Here we go, it's your turn," I tell the chosen beads, and place them around my neck. "Now aren't you lovely," I proudly announce, looking in the mirror. At 11 a.m. there is a knock at the front door, and I let Helen enter. She starts off by putting a wash in, and then makes her way upstairs to tidy the bathroom. I let her do her thing and sit out in the garden and enjoy the sun. Looking around, I realize that my plants have got quite out of control. You couldn't really call it a garden anymore. It was more a growing jungle. Plants everywhere, climbing up each other and attacking the small path. Feeling overwhelmed, I take a deep breath and slowly exhale trying to block out the extent it takes and close my eyes for a moment.

"Mollie!" I'm suddenly startled by a familiar voice calling my name. "Who is that?" I think, and try to get full vision back, but the bright sun has taken my clear sight. "Mollie!" It goes again. I know that voice, but I just cannot place it. A lady with dark curly hair is walking down the path towards me. "Here you are! Helen let me in. How are you? Oh, it's lovely out here, isn't it," she carries on without a break. "Oh, hi, um, yes it is," I confirm frantically, trying to think of her name. It's on my tongue, but I just cannot get it out. She sits down next to me on the bench and leans back and rests her back on the shed wall. "Hmm, this is lovely," she smiles and closes her eyes. She doesn't seem to have noticed that I haven't remembered her name, which calms me down a little. It doesn't take a second and I can feel her eyeing me from the side. "That's a nice necklace you are wearing. I'm glad you have rediscovered them," she smiles sympathetically. I know she is family, she must be, it feels so natural to be close to her. She is not my daughter, so much I can tell. "Oh, and you got your hair done. Wonderful, that was about time," she carries on, studying me from top to bottom. "How dare she say that," I think. "Thank you, that sounds like I was quite a mess," I reply, a little disgusted. She just smiles at me and lays her hand on mine. "How about a cup of tea," she asks.

Inside, Helen is just packing up. "I've hung your wash in the airing cupboard upstairs," Helen tells me. "Barbara, it's lovely to have seen you," she smiles at the lady I couldn't find the name for. "Oh, Barbara, now I've got it. Of course, Barbara, my brother's daughter, my guardian," I think, immediately feeling more at peace. "Well, ladies, I'm off. See you next week, Mollie," Helen waves, and turns for the door. Barbara and I are left alone in the cottage. Barbara makes her way behind the kitchen and pours some fresh water into the kettle and then vanishes into the pantry. I let her do her thing and sit down on one of the chairs next to the kitchen counter. Barbara is soon back with a pack of tea bags in her hand. "Have you had lunch?" She asks me with a worried expression across her face. "Um, lunch? No, I had a large breakfast," I tell her, not really feeling sure if that's correct. "Breakfast, okay. Your pantry looks like it needs some groceries. It's quite empty. How about we go down the town for some lunch and shopping," she asks me. "That would be nice," I admit. Indeed, it would be nice to get out. I'm spending all my time at home, I think. "Good, lets have our tea and then head down the village," she smiles, while placing one bag of tea in each cup.

Down the village, we decide on a small restaurant that serve salads and quiche. The food tastes marvellous, I didn't realize how hungry I was, and my plate is soon empty. "You know Mollie, I was thinking about these meals-on-wheels. I think that would be a really wonderful thing for you. I had a chat with Chris and he agrees. We should try it!" I don't understand what she is talking about. "Meals-on-wheels?" I ask, immediately realizing that Barbara is once again up to something. "Well, it's an organization that delivers cooked meals to peoples' homes. It saves you having to do the cooking. It's very convenient. We could get it organized for every second day. That way you can cook yourself one day and enjoy being served the other day," she brightly smiles. I feel patronised. Why is she telling me what to do? I have survived two world wars, does she think I can't cook for myself! I have accepted Helen. I have to admit it is quite comfortable. But not cooking for myself, where will this lead to. "I'm perfectly happy cooking for myself, I have a garden full of food." There we go now, I've told her. "That's the other topic I wanted to talk to you about. George has some time to spare this weekend. He enjoys gardening, as you know. So we will be back on Sunday and will help you out getting the plants trimmed, they do need it," she tells me with widened eyes. I start to regret that I joined Barbara for lunch. "Well, now that we sorted that, let's go to the supermarket. You need some essentials," she orders and waves to the waitress.

To prove to myself, I cook dinner once I'm back home. I put a chicken breast in the oven, boil some potatoes and stir-up some brown sauce. Just to make sure I don't get distracted, I set an alarm clock to remind me to take the chicken out of the oven on time. All works perfectly, and in the quiet of the cottage, with only the clocks ticking, I enjoy my feast. I pour myself a glass of sherry before I go to bed. I say cheers to myself out into the air, and close my eyes while I feel the liquid make its way down to my tummy, warming every inch of my body. "Hmm, I should make this my new ritual," I giggle.

Content, I lie in bed and enjoy the tickling warm feeling spreading out, reaching every single toe. With a smile on my face I fall asleep, and let myself go into a wonderful pink world. Happily I twirl and dance in my dream. The ground beneath me is soft, and I bounce with every step. It's as if my body was young and free of any pain. Every move I make is supple and rhythmic. I feel more and more daring. "Yes, you can do it," I hear cheerful voices encouraging me, and I do. I lean back to gather all my strength and then run. The soft wind waves through my hair and I cannot help but laugh. The heavenly voices are laughing with me. I bend forward, curl my head towards my breast and do a somersault. My body flies through the air and for a short moment I can see the fluffy pink ground beneath me and then the blue sky above me with bushiest white clouds. I stretch my arms towards them and close my eyes. Softly I land, my arms still stretched out wide. The cushion that caught me starts to slowly turn. Looking up, I can see the sun smiling down at me. Around me is laughter and joy. Little pretty fairies are carrying me and wildly cheering. "You did it, Mollie. You did it! We knew you could do it," their voices call, and then they start to sing the most beautiful melodies. The rays of sunlight are warming me. Soft vines pop their heads out of the cushion beneath me and start to climb up my arms and legs. They are smooth and gentle and twine their way all around me. Luscious green leaves spring out of the stems and unroll themselves. They are as large as tea plates and glitter in the sunlight. They carefully bend themselves back, showing off their long, elegant necks. Large buds enchantingly take the space, and slowly curl themselves up to their full size. The fairies cheer and clap. It's like watching burlesque dancers take the stage. In synchrony, they sway from one side to the other without giving away their inner beauty. Teasing their audience, they open one petal after the other to only give a short insight before quickly closing them again. The cheering around me gets louder and louder until the flowers give way and open themselves fully. Their colours are of indescribable beauty. Yellows, reds, pinks and violets. The blaze of colour overwhelms me and the audience gasps. Carefully, they lay their heavy heads down on my body and decorate me. I am surrounded by the most beautiful scent that can only be made in heaven. The fairies voices whisper to me. "Let go, Mollie, let go. Stay with us, here it's beautiful. Nothing will harm you. You will only feel peace and harmony." Their little hands gently stroke my arms and hair.

Peacefully I turn to one side and remain in my dream world that doesn't scare me.

CHAPTER TWENTY-TWO

I'm in the kitchen making myself some toast with cheese when I see a large car pull up in front of the cottage. A bunch of young men get out. One of them seems to be in the lead. He quickly walks towards my home and knocks on the door. I drop my toast onto my plate and eagerly walk towards the door. I haven't had any visitors for a while, and I'm hungry for company. I don't count Inspector Barbara, and I know it's not my secret dream-world friends. Full of curiosity, I open the door. Four young men are looking at me. The one at the front has the most beautiful bright eyes that could charm any duck off a pond. His large happy smile covers his face. "Nana, it's so nice to see you!" He doesn't wait for me to reply and embraces me. "Nana," I repeat in my mind. "Okay, this must be family. If I could just remember his name. If he is calling me Nana, then this must be my grandson" I tell myself. "These are my friends, you know, the ones I told you about on the telephone last week. This is Tom," he points to the smallest guy. "Then we have Mike and Greg," he says, pointing to the other two. "Oh yes, of course," I lie with a bright smile. I don't mind not really knowing their names, nor not remembering having a telephone conversation, I am just so happy to have visitors. "We'll just unload," my grandson tells me, and says something to the other three in a language I cannot understand. They open the car boot and unload their bags and four skateboards. "Now this is different," I tell myself, watching them.

Inside the cottage, they line up their skateboards and their colourful sneakers – it's quite a sight. "Nana, we'll head down to the fish and chips shop and buy some dinner. You'll take some too, won't you?" My grandson happily calls through the house. "Fish and chips, that sounds nice," I reply. Before I realize what's happening, the four of them have slipped into their shoes and are out on the street. "See you later," he calls, and waves as they walk up the road.

The boys going out gives me time. I need to find out his name. I inspect all the family photos I have in the sitting room. One picture shows three little children. This must be them, these must be my grandchildren. But what about their names, I wonder. Maybe I'll find something on the back of the picture, I think, and undo the frame. And there are their names, neatly written on the back of the picture. Matthew, Kathy and David. "There we go," I smile to myself. I have another look at the picture. Matthew and Kathy have bright eyes. David has deep brown eyes. So it's clear. Matthew is here with his friends. Happy to have worked this out, I walk back into the kitchen and there it is. I've written Matthew in large letters beneath Wednesday. "Is it already Wednesday today?" I ask myself in horror, noticing I haven't crossed off the days for nearly a whole week. I quickly pick up a pen and cross off the dates. My two white pill bottles catch my attention. Have I been taking them? I'm not sure. I shake them, and they sound full. "Well, I better take one each. I'm sure Barbara would have said something if I had been going for longer without taking them," I calm myself and take a pill from each bottle before turning back to the kitchen counter. My toast is lying on its plate where I left it, looking very dry. "Well, I wont need that anymore. I'm getting fish and chips," I merrily tell myself aloud. I put my pills down and empty my plate into the kitchen bin. A foul smell hits me and I jerk my head up, away from the bin. "Uh, that's bad!" Squinting my eyes, I look back down. "It looks alive in there, I better get this sorted before they come back." I quickly lift the black plastic bag out of its container, tie a knot, take it to the back of the cottage and drop it into one of the large waste bins. Back in the kitchen, I frantically search for a new bin bag. "There must be some somewhere. Ugh, Helen must have put them somewhere else," I argue to myself, while pushing piles of pots and pans from one side to the other. "What are all these things?" I wonder. "Oh, they'll be useful for the gardening," I look admiringly at some empty, white plastic butter bowls. "What are you doing?" Another voice within me asks in a harsh tone. "I don't know! What am I doing?" I reply, feeling like a child caught trying to secretly steal some chocolate. "I'm definitely looking for something. Okay, one step after the other," I try to sort myself out, and take a step back. "It looks quite a mess in here," another voice tells me, while my eyes frantically scan the shelves looking for clues. "That's not the point and anyway, I'm a gardener, I need these things," I argue back. "So what are they doing in the pantry?" My other voice cheekily asks back. "I'm not talking to you!" I decide, and stamp back into the kitchen and am just able to stop myself from stumbling over the open bin. "What are you doing here?" I shout at the open, white bin. "Oh gosh, you don't have a bag. I'll fetch one. Now, where are they?" I think a moment and decide to look in the cupboard beneath the sink. "Here we go," I pull out a roll of black bin liners and tear one off with a wrench. Hovering over the bin, the foul smell hits me again. "Ugh, that's bad!" With squinting eyes, I look at the bin. Brown coloured liquid has formed across the bottom. Wrinkling my nose, I pick up the container and make my way out into the garden, making sure to hold it as far as possible from me. Once outside, I put it down on the ground and fetch the hose, and spray the bins inside with fresh water. "Much better," I tell myself, admiring my handiwork. Chatting sounds from inside the cottage make me jump. I peer through the window and see some young men walking into my kitchen. "Who are they?" I wonder, feeling a little silly standing outside in my slippers with a dripping wet bin in my hand. "Nana?" I hear one of the men shout. "Oh, I must have visitors," I think to myself, and quickly try to remember who they are. A young man with bright eyes appears at the back door. "Nana, we are back. Join us before the fish gets cold," he smiles. "Oh yes, lovely," I smile back. "I was just doing this," I gesture to the bin and the hose, not really remembering exactly what I was doing. "Let me take that," he offers, and quickly winds up the hose and carries the bin into the kitchen for me. Luckily, the black bag is lying on the kitchen counter giving me the much-needed reminder of what to do next. "Put this one in there for me, will you," I ask, feeling relieved to be on top of things again. Two white pills lying next to my cup catch my attention, and I quickly pop them into my mouth and swallow them with a gulp of cold tea. My grandson doesn't notice. He is too busy bending down and fixing the black plastic bag into the white bin.

I'm up early the next day. At first I don't really know why. My alarm clock says 7:30 a.m. and I feel persuaded by my inner voice to turn to the other side and see if I can escape a little longer into my pink, cotton wool dream. But another voice, I would like to call it the reasonable me, tells me to get up. Rubbing my eyes, I make my way to the bathroom. Four toothbrushes are lined up on the window sill. "That's odd," I think and wash my face with icy water. Feeling refreshed, I decide to go downstairs and investigate. Both the guest room doors are closed. "That must mean I have guests," I tell myself, and make my way downstairs. Four colourful sneakers are standing next to each other and four skateboards are lined along the wall. "Now, this is interesting, let's see what's on my calendar," I think, grabbing the newspaper that is sticking halfway through the letterbox, and walk into the kitchen. The days of the month that have already passed are neatly marked off. Beneath Wednesday, Matthew is written in large letters. The newspaper in my hand tells me it's Thursday. "So Matthew arrived yesterday," I tell myself, and pick-up a black pen and mark off the Wednesday. Feeling proud of myself, I pour fresh water into the kettle and make a cup of tea.

The cottage is silent and I sit and enjoy it becoming more and more alive with every sip. Outside, I can hear birds chirping and, in the distance, car engines muttering, transporting their drivers to work. The clinking noise of glass bottles bouncing against each other reminds me that the milkman must be here. I quickly jump up and open the door. "Hey there, Mollie," the milkman cheerfully greets me. "Hello, er, John," I reply, feeling relieved that the man has a name tag on his jacket. "Could you give me an extra bottle today? I have visitors," I proudly explain. "Sure, Mollie, let me fetch you one." He turns and walks back to his small milk float. While I wait, all the things that I will need to be able to offer my guests for breakfast go through my mind. "Here you go," he says, handing me an extra bottle of milk. "Oh, thank you," I reply, a little lost in my thoughts. He smiles kindly, waves and carries on to the next house. Back indoors, I put my milk away and get dressed. I need to go shopping before they are all up.

"Nana, would you like me to help you clear some of the things in the backroom," calls Matthew from the sitting room. "What does he mean?" I wonder, and decide to join him. "We'll be leaving tomorrow. So we should get all the things done that you need help with today," he smiles at me. My tummy turns. "They're leaving tomorrow," I repeat in my mind. A wave of sadness overcomes me, but I hold it back - I don't want him to notice. Looking around, I can't deny that my storage could cave in on me any minute. Every shelf is bursting, with not one surface left empty. What on earth have I been up to, I think. Matthew is watching me with bright eyes. "I can clear away some of these plastic pots. I don't think you need them. And the piles of old newspapers, I will carry them all out and leave them next to the road. The bin men will pick them up. That will give you some space," he explains, while wandering through the backroom and examining the inside of pots and boxes. "Okay, let me know if I can help you with anything," I offer, in a resigned manner. "Don't worry, Nana, it will be much better afterwards. You'll see," he happily calms me, and starts lifting up boxes.

After my grandson and his friends have left, I return to everyday life. Gradually, day for day, I've been getting up later and later. The days have lost their value. My only routine is the cleaning day with Helen and my weekly shopping with my neighbour, Nancy. For these two events only, I get up early, put on fresh clothes and wear a matching pearl necklace. I don't want anyone to notice that I am getting more and more forgetful, and am living in my own dream world. I'm determined to stand on my own two feet. I'm fine and absolutely convinced of that. And anyway, everybody has his or her own little dream world. I just wish I could get on with it and leave, I think. "I don't understand what the Lord is messing at. I am fed up and want to go and be with my daughter and husband," I tell the stuffed cat, a cuddly toy that I bought down in the town to keep me company. The cat, which is sitting in a pale wicker basket next to my armchair, just stares back at me with its two black shiny button eyes. Its brown fur is sticking out in all directions and it looks like it has walked through a bush backwards. "I just cannot understand the reason for me to have to wait all these years alone, Mr Cat," I carry on, without expecting an answer, and look out of the window into the dark of the night. "You should be closing those curtains, Mollie," my reasonable-me tells me. With a grumble, I get out of my armchair and pull the curtains closed. "While I'm standing, I might as well fetch my sherry," I smile at the cat and dance towards the pantry with a thrill of anticipation. Before reaching the pantry door, I decide to make a twirl to elegantly finalize my steps. The four walls of the cottage flash by and I feel a breeze stroke my cheek. My short legs tremble and I just manage to catch myself on the kitchen sink. A cold sweat runs down my back. "Oh dear, what was that?" I pant to myself, and dab my forehead with the back of my hand. "Well, you're not 20 any more, are you now," I scold myself, and lean against the cupboard and wait until my breath finds its rhythm again. "This isn't putting me off my sherry, you know," I call out into the room with a giggle.

Later that night, I fall asleep feeling the warmth of the sherry. The cold sweat has dried, and my moment of weakness is forgotten as I enter my dream world. Beneath my feet, I can feel the softest moss, it's as if I'm bouncing with every step I take. The lushest green shines between my toes. Nothing aches and there are no tired muscles or churning bones. I am like a feather, light and free, bouncing from one patch of soft moss to the other. Around me, majestic trees guard my path, sheltering me from the evil of the world. The sky above is clear and blue, with not a cloud in sight. Fine beams of sunlight play with my scarlet skin. Stroking my arm, I feel young, no wrinkles, only soft tissue. Delighted by the feeling, I place my face into my hands and stroke upwards towards my cheekbones. It's the silkiest feeling. My skin is plump and soft. Feeling alive, I stretch my arms to the sky and twirl around. Colourful butterflies join me and flap their delicate wings, spreading golden stardust full of magic. The scent is heavenly and I can feel myself sparkle. Gently, I'm picked up from the ground and carried to the top of the tall trees. The golden corns of stardust slowly grow. "My little fairies," I whisper to myself, watching the corns take shape. "I knew that you would be here," I shyly smile, feeling deep happiness. Little hands gently comb my hair, making me feel content and safe. "Mollie, Mollie," a heavenly voice sings to me. "We have kept a treasure for you. Look, look!" the voice whispers. Next to me, there's an old shoe box decorated with colourful autumn leaves. There are two purple letters in the middle of the box, an M and a P. "Mary Price, my maiden name," I announce, stroking the weathered paper with my finger. My fairies look at me with big, wide eyes. "Open the box. Open the box," they shout excitedly. Carefully, I lift the lid. The cardboard is stuck a little on one corner, but eventually gives way. My childhood treasures are inside of the box, all carefully lined up next to each other. The smooth dark pebble immediately catches my eye, and I pick it up. It feels smooth and cool lying in my hand.

For a minute, I close my eyes and relive my memories. I am with my brothers, who sadly passed away many years ago. But now we are young again, and cheerfully shouting and screaming while running through the tall grass. Les and

Fred overtake me, but I don't mind. I like to watch them run in front of me and see their hair bobbing up and down. I stretch my arms and let the wind carry me. We are so free. The world seems to stand open to us. My thumb strokes across the fine surface of the pebble and a tear rolls down my cheek. A little hand catches it before it drops from the edge of my face and then gently dries the path it left behind. "Don't cry, Mollie," a little voice whispers. "The moment you're thinking of isn't yours anymore, its gone! But the memory, the memory cannot be taken. Enjoy feeling the love you had. You can always call upon those and decide to feel them deep in your heart. Nobody can take that from you," the fairy smiles, laying her tiny hand on mine. I sniff, and rub the stone a last time before laying it back in the box.

Fine embroidery catches my eye. It's a white tissue with flowery stitching around the sides. My eyes are glued to the material. "Take it, Mollie," the gentle voice persuades me. I look at the fairy, and she reassuringly nods at me. Carefully, I take the delicate fabric in my hand and smell its scent. A fine smell of roses surrounds me and I close my eyes. My wedding day. My heart trembles and I quickly open my eyes. The fairy is kindly watching me. "Let it go, Mollie. Enjoy the memory, that's yours. I'll stay with you. Feel my hand on yours and know I'm here," she reassuringly pats her hand on mine. I hesitate, but feel that I cannot resist, and close my eyes and let myself go back in time again. I am sitting in the zinc tub enjoying the heavenly scent of rose soap that my mother rubs over my back. The delicious, intruding scent takes me away to the chapel. I am wearing my long, white wedding dress. The silk material plays against my skin as I walk up the church steps. The door is open and a fresh breeze blows through my carefully combed curls. And there he is, Jack Meredith, my future husband, waiting down the aisle for me. He is so happy, so full of love. I stretch out my hand towards him and so does he. The tip of our fingers meet and I can feel his warmth filling every cell of my body. I cannot help but smile, feeling the electricity run through me. "The moment is gone. But the memory is mine," I mutter, and allow the pillow to dry my tears.

CHAPTER TWENTY-THREE

My alarm clock wakes me at 8:00 a.m. Groaning, I reach over and turn it off. Next to the clock, a piece of paper says "Helen". "Urgh, it must be Wednesday," I say aloud, and push my feet out of the bed. After washing myself, I decide on a brown skirt and purple knitted top. Going through my jewellery box looking for matching pearls, a small velvet box catches my attention. I know what it is. It's my wedding ring that Jack Meredith gave me on the day of our blessing. I open the lid and look down at the slim wedding band, and inspect the ring in the sunlight shining through my bedroom window. It's a simple band without any knick-knacks. My ring finger is taken by the wedding band that I shared with Bill. He was the love of my life, no doubt. He is the partner I miss most, and who gave me the greatest gift ever, Sue. I would never exchange him with anybody else. But Jack was also a part of my life. A memory I don't want to miss. I decide not to think too much about it. There is space for both so I slip my second wedding ring onto my finger and go downstairs for breakfast.

It's a wonderful day outside, and I enjoy some toast and tea with the backdoor open, letting the fresh air silently sweep through the living room. My head is aching slightly. My feeling tells me it's coming from my short moment of weakness last night. Strangely enough, I can remember that happening very well. "Some fresh air and a walk would probably do me good. What do you think, Mr Cat?" I ask the ginger cuddly toy, who is silently sitting in its basket. "I could pick some of those red roses in the garden and take them down to the cemetery," I carry on, speaking aloud. Leaning back, I rest my head and watch the street through the window. All is calm. The picture in front of me doesn't change. A wave of tiredness overcomes me and I close my eyes for a moment. My right thumb and index finger twirl my rings back and forth. "Come on old girl, let's get up before thing-a-bob is here. You don't want to be caught snoozing with your breakfast plate on your knees," my reasonable-me orders. "Ah," I take a deep breath, clap the plate on my knee and get to my feet. I do still feel a little shaky, I have to admit, but I am sure the air will do me good. "Now, who's coming?" I ask myself and check the calendar. Helen is written into every Wednesday's field. "Helen? It rings a bell. But what does she do?" I ask myself, feeling a little puzzled. "I definitely should know this," I scold myself. "Never mind, I will find out," I calm myself, feeling too tired to carry on thinking about it.

While washing up my plate and cup, I watch the bird house out in the garden. There are no birds there. But that's no wonder, as there are no leftovers waiting for them. "When did I last leave something out for them?" I wonder to myself. But it's impossible for me find an answer. I have no clue. "I will take some of this for them," I decide with a smile, and fish a slice of toast out of the bag that is lying on the kitchen counter and tear it into little pieces. "I anyway wanted to go out into the garden, didn't I. Now, what did I want to do in the garden?" I ask myself. "Oh," I look down at my hands and spot the little pieces of toast. "Of course, the bird house, this will be nice for them." Feeling content to have found my answer, I walk out into the garden.

The bird house is standing on a tall pole to protect the little visitors from cats. It's quite a stretch for me to place the breadcrumbs on the house's ledge, standing on tiptoe. The sun blinds me and takes away my sight. The blue sky and the bird house fade away, and I can only see bright yellow light. I'm forced to close my eyes for a second. In the dark, my hand tries to feel its way onto the wooden ledge. My legs start to shake and a cold sweat spreads all the way down my neck and back within seconds. My mouth goes dry, I feel dizzy and my nails try to dig into the old wood to hold myself. But it's too late, I cannot hold myself and I feel my body collapse like a tower of playing cards. One muscle after the other gives in, and everything goes black. Three or four sparks shoot across the dark and I am gone.

"Mollie, Mollie, do you hear me," echoes in my head. All is still dark, and I have no clue where I could be or what happened. The only thing I can feel is a terrible headache. "Oh dear, oh dear. Mollie, can you say anything?" I can feel my head being lifted and placed against something soft. A taste of iron in my mouth disturbs me. I move my lips to say something, but my words don't make their way out. Instead, I feel sand corns churning between my teeth. All I can think is that I need a drink. A hand gently strokes my forehead and I try to open my eyes. At first, all is just white. Then, slowly, shapes start to form. Trees branches, a corner of a garden shed, a bird house on a pole and a face. As my sight gradually recovers, I can make out more details and colours. The face comes into focus, but I cannot place it. "Mollie, my goodness, you had me in shock. Are you okay?" The face goes on. "Oh, my head," I manage. "Oh dear yes, I can imagine. You must have passed out and hit your head. You have a cut on your leg that doesn't look good. Do you think you can manage to get up?" The lady asks. That is all I can make out. It's definitely a woman. I feel her hands grasp under my armpits and lift me. "You're going to have to help me, Mollie," she gasps. I try to activate my muscles and help her get me back to my feet. My legs tremble, I just can't stop it and feel relieved that she doesn't let me go. With her arms around me, we walk step-by-step back into the cottage and, indoors, she helps me sit down in the armchair. Once seated, I collapse back into the chair and rest my aching head. "I'll fetch you an Aspirin and a bandage. I'll be right back," she tells me, looking worried. I wish I could remember her name. She is so kind.

My memory is blank, and even though I try to go through my steps I can't remember what happened. "Here you go, take this with some water," says the lady, handing me two white pills and a glass of water. I do as I am told, and swallow them down in one gulp. "Now, let me have a look at your leg." She kneels down in front of me. Her forehead creases. "Sorry, Mollie, I will have to take your stocking off," she looks up at me sympathetically and then carefully removes my left sock without waiting for my answer. She dabs some disinfectant that stings all up my leg and then gently places some tissue over the wound and wraps a bandage around my leg. "There you go," she smiles at me sympathetically. "You look very pale, would you like to have a lie down," she asks, and stretches her hand towards me. "I will help you upstairs," she offers. I don't feel my old self. Some rest could help, I think, and thankfully reach for her hand.

"There you go. Do you feel comfortable?" She asks, while laying the blanket over me. I just nod and try to smile at her. "I will come back in a few hours and see how you are going, all right?" She asks, standing back from the bed. Once again I nod and turn on my side. I feel so tired that I can hardly keep my eyes open, and immediately fall into a deep sleep. In my dreams, everything feels just out of my reach. It's as if a cloud keeps everything just a step away from me. Nothing makes sense. I can hear voices whisper, but I can't understand what they are saying. It frustrates me and I frantically try to open the grey curtains that surround me, but I'm not successful. Every movement is punished by a stinging pain that shoots through my body.

I awake with a dry mouth and throat. It feels as if I have been shouting for hours. On my bedside table, I make out a glass of water, and quickly sit up and enjoy the feeling of the cool fluid moisturising my vocal chords. "Ah, that's better," I gasp. My alarm clock next to the bed shows 2:00 p.m. "Oh, gosh. What am I doing in bed at this time," I wonder, and notice a piece of paper next to the clock with Helen written on it. "Now, that is strange. She should have been here by now. Did she just let me sleep?" I ask myself, and decide to get out of bed. "Oww, my leg hurts." Looking down, I realize I am fully dressed and have a blood-stained bandage around my left leg. I don't know what to make of my situation, and decide I need a cup of tea to help sort it all out.

Every step down the stairs thumps in my head. A knock at the front door makes me jump. "Who could that be?" I wonder, and open the door. A young lady with red hair smiles at me. "Nana," she happily greets me, but her smile is brief and quickly vanishes. A worried expression takes over her face. Nervously, she looks over to a man who is standing next to her. "Hello, Mollie. Are you okay?" He asks me, scanning me from top to bottom. I just cannot place them. "They seem to know me, and I do feel they are family. But who?" I wonder. "Never mind, play the game and you'll work it out," I order myself. "Oh, hello. Oh this is a surprise. Come in." I open the door and let them in. The man puts his arm around me. "You better sit down, Mollie. Let me have a look at your leg," he tells me, guiding me to a chair in the kitchen. They both gather around and inspect me. A blonde lady and a young man with bright eyes join them. "How many are there," I ask myself. "That doesn't look good, Mollie," the man gestures. The young lady with red hair points to my left hand. "Look Dad, Nana's hand is swollen." She looks upset. "Uhm, I had a fall in the garden," I start to explain. "When did this happen," the man asks me. "When did it happen, when did it happen?" I repeat in my mind, but I find no answer. "Oh, it must have been this morning or yesterday," I try to explain, realising it sounds a little odd. They all look at me, and then at each other. The young lady with the red hair and the man seem to be talking to each other without words. A knock at the door makes them all jump and turn their heads. "Oh, hello. I'm Helen. I do the cleaning for Mollie," a dark-haired lady explains, walking into the kitchen. "Hi, I'm Chris. I'm Mollie's son-in-law and this is Marika my wife, Kathy my daughter and Matthew my son. David, my other son, will be here any minute too. The three of them are Mollie's grandchildren," he explains. "So they are family," I think to myself, and feel much more comfortable, even though I couldn't follow all the names and relations. "Oh, I am so glad you're here," says Helen, looking relieved. "I found Mollie in the garden this morning. She must have passed out and fell. I didn't know what to do, so I gave her some aspirins, cleaned the wound on her leg and put her to bed," she explains, looking nervous. "You should have took her to hospital or at least to the doctor," the man tells her, looking quite annoyed. Helen looks down at the ground. "Well, now that you're here, I guess I'm not needed anymore. I'll be back next week for the cleaning," she murmurs without looking up, and quickly leaves the cottage. The four discuss something together. They all look worried. "Hi there," a happy voice rings into the cottage. A lady with dark curls and a young man walk into the kitchen, smiling all over their faces. "Barbara!" the red haired lady and the man both call. "Oh, it's so nice to see you. Did you arrive okay?" The dark curly-haired lady greets them with a big hug. "I met David on the way here," she smiles and looks at the young man who arrived with her. This is like being at the train station. All these people coming and going, I think to myself, and quite enjoy the attention. "Barbara," the man says, and gestures to my leg and hand. "Helen, the cleaning lady, was here a minute ago and told us that Mollie had a fall in the garden," he explains, looking serious. "Oh, Mollie dear, what happened?" Barbara asks me, kneeling down so our eyes meet. I know that I know this happy person. I also know that she is regularly with me, but I wouldn't have been able to place her name if the man hadn't used it. "Don't worry, I am okay, it's not that bad," I try to calm them all with a smile. I am definitely not keen on going to hospital. I don't like people poking around at me. Barbara stands back up and faces the man. "What do you think we should do?" She asks. "We just talked about it before you arrived. It's best if we take her to the hospital to get everything checked. Kathy and myself can take her," he finishes. "Yes, that will be best. I can wait up at the Longmynd and inform the guests," she agrees. I've no clue what she is talking about. "Longmynd? Guests? Have I forgotten something," I wonder to myself. Barbara turns to me. "Oh dear, Mollie, we wanted to surprise you with a 90th birthday party at the Longmynd Hotel. I'm so sorry." Barbara kneels down in front of me. She sincerely looks sad. "Hopefully the doctors will be able to figure everything out and we can celebrate your birthday later tonight," she clutches my hand and smiles.

30 minutes later, we are in the hospital, and a doctor is shining his little torch into my eyes. "Mollie, do you know where you are?" The doctor asks me. I look at him a little puzzled. Why is he asking such a question, I think. "I'm at the hospital, aren't I," I tell him. "Do you know who these two people are?" He gestures with his notepad to the man and the young lady with red hair. I feel pressurised. "I don't

like his questions, I don't like this doctor and anyway, he's far too young to be doing this job properly," I grumble to myself. His bright eyes watch me while he waits for my answer. "Why don't you ask them?" I tell him, feeling quite clever to have found my way out. He turns his little torch off and slips it into the pocket of his white coat. "I would like you to tell me Mollie," he insists. How dare he, I think, feeling colour shoot into my face. "They are my family," I tell him in a tone that doesn't accept any contradiction. "Have you been taking your medication?" He carries on. "What does he mean? Do I take medication?" I ask myself. "Yes," I answer. "Do you have all three bottles?" He asks, while studying my chart. "Yes, I do," I reply. Now these are the questions I prefer, I think to myself, feeling that I am doing quite well. "Who is Barbara?" He asks me, looking up from the chart. "Uhm, well. I'm sure it's there on the paper you have," I point towards the chart he is holding. "Why do you think that?" He replies, and sits down on the corner of the bed. I feel as if the walls of the room are coming closer and closer. It was all going so well. Why did he change the questions, I think, feeling trapped. "I'm sure it is. You don't need to ask me questions you know the answer to," I tell him, and I turn my head away from him as a sign that the conversation is ended. "Okay, Mollie, we will be running some tests on you. Your granddaughter, Kathy," he gestures to the young, red-haired lady, "will help you if needed. You will have to stay here some days. It looks like you had a stroke. We want to be sure you have the right medication to recover and that this doesn't happen again," he explains, in a businesslike manner. "What? A stroke? Stay in hospital and miss my birthday party?" shoots through my mind. I can't believe what is happening. "We will first see to your leg. The wound needs cleaning and your wrist is badly bruised. The swelling will gradually reduce, but we need to make sure you keep calm," he explains with a sympathetic smile. "Don't worry, Mollie, you'll be fine," he calms me, and lays his hand on my shoulder for a second. All seems settled.

The aspirins that Helen gave me are losing their effect, and I can feel a stinging pain at the side of my head. I am quite glad to be able to just lie down and not move. Resting my head, I try to remember exactly what Barbara said about my party. I cannot put it together, and eventually let the thought go. The growing pain in my head has won.

I have no idea how long I've been in hospital. I don't like the doctors. They are always trying to examine some part of me. It's not how I grew up, and I'm not used to it. But the nurses are nice and I enjoy their attention and the short moments of chitchat. Today, they got me dressed properly. I cannot remember the reason, but I know they told me, and I felt all right about what ever it was. The lady with the curly dark hair visited me and brought me some fresh clothes. She is very nice, and I kept on repeating her name in my mind until I got tired. For a while it stuck, but today I only know that she is family.

"Mollie, dear, Chris and Kathy are here to pick you up", Nurse Mary joyfully announces, approaching my room with a man and a young lady with red hair. "This is Chris, your son-in-law and this young lady is Kathy, your grand-daughter," nurse Mary introduces my guests. I can feel my cheeks flame. How dare she be so straightforward! She could have been a little less direct in front of my family, I think to myself, and scold her with a nasty look. I study my grand-daughter. She is very slim and pretty. She looks a little nerv-ous clutching her handbag, and seems unsure about what she should do. Her red hair plays around her face and makes her look like an angel. She reminds me of someone. I just cannot put my finger on it. My son-in-law, Chris, is a happy man. He has full cheeks and doesn't seem to have any fear of contact. "This is your bag with your personal belongings, Mollie. I am sure your son-in-law will carry that for you," she winks at Chris. He seems pleased by the nurse's attention, and smiles back. Nurse Mary walks straight towards me and embraces me. "We will miss you, Mollie. You take good care of yourself." Her blue eyes twinkle as she takes a last look at me before heading out of the door.

CHAPTER TWENTY-FOUR

Chris drives, and I'm allowed to sit next to him as his co-driver. Not that I am much help steering the car or guiding the way, as I have no clue where we are heading for, but I enjoy having the full view out of the large front window. Kathy sits on the back seat and is very quiet. Chris and I chat about all sorts. I am not always sure, but now and then I get the feeling I'm repeating myself. Asking the same question over and over again. I am not really sure about my observation, and the thought only bothers me for the short moment when I realize either Chris or Kathy are looking at me perplexed. We are driving through an area with tall hills and luscious green woodland. The area is beautiful and I feel at home, and I try to read the road signs whenever possible to try and find out where we are. At a large crossing, we stop and wait for the traffic light to turn to green. There are some small detached houses on one side of the road. On the other side, on my side, there is a bridge crossing over a railway station. There is a large sign welcoming us to Church Stretton. I repeat the name in my mind. "I know this place," I tell myself, and quietly try to make out why. The feeling nags me that we should be turning left and driving over this bridge. But Chris has steered the car onto the middle lane that leads straight ahead. The palms of my hands go damp and I feel uncomfortable. I breathe deeply to calm myself, but I cannot get enough air. I cannot explain what is going on and try to hide my outburst by looking out of the passenger window. This doesn't help though, as I have the bridge, the sign and the road leading up into the little village right in my view. People are walking up and down the pavement with shopping bags, parcels or bunches of flowers. Some have toddlers clinging to their free hand. A normal, everyday life in a village. I feel that I would like to be part of this scenery. I think I belong here, but I cannot explain why. This innocent picture of life in front of me makes me feel sad. Feeling I can't watch it any longer, I stare down to my skirt and iron the pretty material. It has gone very quiet inside of the car. The tension is so high it could be cut.

Chris and Kathy brought me home. After a cup of tea they left, and told me that they would be back tomorrow. It's strange, my home is really large and I feel I could get lost any minute. There are several sitting rooms and a large dining room. "Did I really live in such a spacious place?" I ask myself. It feels wrong, and I surely didn't have people that did all the work for me. All is very odd and frustrating, as I cannot work it out and therefore just have to go with it.

The people taking care of me are very nice and have little name tags on their shirts. This makes my problem of not remembering names anymore much easier. I just have to think of reading the tags.

What hits me as very strange is that I have roommates. I mean, I have my own area of privacy but, for example in the television or dining room, there are other people. They are all my age and don't take too much notice of me. This observation tells me I'm not at home, I am somewhere else and stuck, because I cannot explain what is wrong. Anger builds up inside me. I feel furious and frustrated at the same time. "How dare they!" I shout to myself, feeling my hands turn to fists beside me. "I'm going to work out what is going on. They will see, a little rest and I will be fine again. Time will show," I promise myself.

"Mollie," a happy looking blond lady with a name tag telling me she is called Jane interrupts my thoughts. "Let me help you upstairs to your room. You must be terribly tired after such a long day," she smiles at me, and offers me her hand. "What?" I say to myself, feeling totally puzzled by this offer. "Is she telling me it's time for me to go to bed? Damn Miss Smiley, we will see about that," I think determinedly. "I'm sorry, who are you, young lady?" I ask her in a serious tone. "Oh, I am sorry, Mollie, I haven't introduced myself, have I." Her cheeks go a little pink. Her happy nature is going to make this discussion difficult, I can feel it. "I am Jane, the night care attendant. I will be helping you get all you need for a good night's sleep," she smiles. "Well, I have a sherry before I go to bed," I reply in a strict tone. I'm a little surprised about myself. "A sherry? Do I? But of course I do. See, I am nearly back to my old self," I smile triumphantly, and congratulate myself in my mind. "Oh, now that's a nice habit, Mollie. Um, let me see what's on your chart. I'll be right back," she quickly turns and leaves the room. "Ha, you'd better be. And make it a big glass," I shout inwardly, feeling totally in control. "This could actually be fun," I think, and carry on watching the talk show that is running on the television. I didn't remember what I was watching and carefully listen to the discussions to try and work out what it is all about. There are two women and two men arguing about some topic I cannot quite make out. There seems to be a lot of commotion about something. Gosh, this is complicated. I don't like their outfits, I think, feeling a little tired. The women are dressed in grey and navy business suits with trousers that make them look like men. Not my generation at all. My eyelids are getting heavy and are dropping down towards my lower lid. Any minute now I'm going to drop off. I can feel my feet warming up and my whole body leaning heavily back into the armchair. "Here we go, Mollie!" Says a blonde lady, handing me a small glass with dark liquid. "You're absolutely right, dear. Your granddaughter left you a lovely bottle for your nightcaps," she smiles. Feeling sleepy, I don't understand what is going on. "Oh, what's this? Is this my medication?" I ask the lady. Her arm that is stretched towards me covers her nametag. "It's your sherry that you just asked for," she blinks. "I drink sherry? Oh okay, thank you." I take the glass and scold myself for my reply. I look up at her through my lashes and try to read her expression. She doesn't seem irritated. I can read Jane on her name tag. She kindly lays her hand on my shoulder for a moment and strokes me. "I will be back in 10 minutes, okay?" She says, but doesn't wait for my answer and just turns and leaves the room. Back in 10 minutes. I wonder for what, I think, and carefully place my lips on the brim of the glass. The sherry is sweet and sticky. I lean back and enjoy the warm feeling making its way down into my tummy.

10 minutes later, I let Jane take me up to my room and help me get changed. I am just too tired to complain. "Just this once," I promise myself, and slip under the covers and immediately fall into a deep sleep. My fairy friends comb my hair and sing sweet lullabies that make me feel comfortable and safe. Here I am at home and warm. I don't want to wake up. I could stay like this forever. "But could I really?" I ask myself in my dream. Isn't there somewhere else I wanted to go? A pulling feeling inside of me tells me there is something else I wanted. Loved ones I miss and want to be with. I am sure about that, even though I cannot name them. They are somewhere and that's where I want to go to, I know it. I know it.

The next day, a lady called Sophie wakes me up. I don't like this and turn to the other side keeping my eyes closed tightly, hoping to signal that she should leave. But it doesn't help. She is determined to get me up and into the bath. "Come on, Mollie. A warm bath is waiting for you, dear," she tries to persuade me. Oh God, what is all this fuss about, I think, still not opening my eyes. "Why is everyone intruding into my privacy," I ask myself. Sophie starts tugging my blanket. "Don't you have anything else to do," I snarl, sitting up in bed with my arms crossed in front of my chest. My reaction surprises myself, but Sophie looks relaxed. "No, I don't," she answers without any signs of pity, and reaches for my dressing gown that is hanging on the back of my room door. She holds the pale pink gown ready for me. "It's a little chilly. I think you should put this on," she gestures. "No, I am not, I am fine," I fire back. "Suit yourself but don't complain on the way to the bathroom," she warns me, and hangs the dressing gown back onto its hanger. "Ready?" She asks me and opens the bedroom door. Now that I am too furious to sleep I give way, and get out of bed and stamp all the way to the bathroom following her. A white bathtub is half-filled with steaming water. There is a chair that is attached to the tub, looking really odd. "You can take off your nighty and sit in the chair. That is the most safest way into the bath," she orders. What! Take off my clothes in front of you. What is this lady thinking of, I think, disgusted. "You can wait outside. I am fine doing this by myself," I tell her, holding my head as high as I can. "Look, Mollie, it's my job to make sure you're safely cleaned and dressed. I respect your privacy. You can wash yourself, that's fine, but I need to make sure you don't fall and hurt yourself getting into the bath. So please let me help you," she asks me in a softer tone. I pout and cross my arms, hugging myself. Sophie just stands still and waits. "Ah, this is leading nowhere," I realise to myself. I might as well get it behind me, I think, resigning. Sophie seems to realise this, and takes a step towards me. "Look, Mollie, this is going to be our daily routine together. I know its not easy at the beginning, but you'll get used to it, I promise. It will be okay," she reassures me, while helping me out of my nighty and into the chair. "Ready?" she asks me, taking a remote control into her hand. I just nod and she presses a button. The chair slowly moves down into the bath's warm water. That feels nice, I think to myself. Sophie was right, it is a chilly day and I have to admit that I was close to turning blue standing next to the tub, pouting. Sophie keeps her word and waits outside until I have finished washing myself.

Breakfast is served in the dining room. Scrambled eggs with toast and tea. It's delicious. I cannot remember when I last had a cooked breakfast. While enjoying every bite, I watch my roommates. Maybe housemates would actually be the more appropriate description. Most of them are in my age group. I would even say that I am one of the most senior inhabitants with my 90-plus years. There is not much conversation going on between the people eating breakfast. Everyone seems caught up with his or her own thoughts. There is one man who is very much focused on the carers who are rushing in and out of the room making sure every-body gets their medication and the required nourishment. He is constantly calling them to his table. When they give in and attend him, he immediately tries to hold their hand. He doesn't like them leaving. On another table, two ladies are sitting together. Even though they are not speaking a lot, they seem comfortable with each other. Both of them are elegantly dressed and are wearing pearls matching their clothes. I feel across my chest and am glad I discover that I have mine on too. The one lady has her handbag with her. It is dangling from one side of her chair. It looks like she is ready to go somewhere, as if she has something to do right after breakfast. "Here is your medication, Mollie," says a kind looking nurse, handing me a paper cup with some pills in it. "Do I take all of these?" I ask, astonished by the amount. "Yes, those are all yours," she smiles. "If you want, I can sit you with those ladies tomorrow." She nods towards the two ladies with pearl necklaces. "I think you would make good friends," she lightly nudges me. I like this nurse, and cannot help but smile at her. While swallowing the pills I look for her name tag. Abigail it reads. Abigail. Abigail, I repeat in my mind. I want to be able to remember her name. "You can give me that," she holds her hand towards the now-empty paper cup.

After breakfast, I'm put into a group that is making paper cut-outs. I can choose between five different coloured papers. The green one catches my eye and reminds me of something I cannot formulate. I follow the instructions and fold my green sheet of paper several times before taking the scissors and cutting shapes out. We end up sticking the paper cuts into our own personal scrapbooks. My piece of art looks lovely against the white backing. The page is filled with the luscious green colour, only broken by the little white dots that I cut out.

Abigail fetches me after lunch. "Mollie, dear, you have visitors. Your son-in-law, Chris, and your granddaughter, Kathy, are here. Would you all like to sit in the front room?" She kindly asks. Chris and Kathy nod and Abigail takes my hand. I am too confused to answer. "Chris and Kathy," goes though my mind. I am sure I know them. "What did Abigail say they are?" I ask myself, but I've already forgotten. "I will fetch you some tea, all right?" Abigail smiles. "That would be lovely," Chris and Kathy reply simultaneously. The three of us sit down. The way they look and sit around me makes me feel as if I am at an interview. I hope that they are not going to ask me questions. "How was your first night," Chris asks me. "Here we go," I think. "My first night?" I wonder what he is talking about. "Oh, its very nice, isn't it," I go along with him, hoping to hit the nail on its head. "Yes, it's nice here, we think so too and are happy with the choice," Kathy answers shyly, smiling at me. "The nurses seem very nice too," she adds, a little unsure. Abigail is back with three cups of steaming black tea and a plate of biscuits. "Here you are. Let me know if you need anything else won't you." She places the tray down on a coffee table next to us and hands me a cup. "Uh, that's hot. Lovely," I say cuddling the cup with both of my hands. "Would you like a biscuit?" Chris asks, and stretches the white plate with a nice selection of creamy treats. There are some pink coloured finger-size ones that catch my attention and I quickly take one before anyone else has the chance. "Hmm, this is good," I marvel to myself, enjoying the strawberry cream filling. Once I've finished, I wash down the crumbs that are stuck to my teeth with the warm tea and look up. "Oh, who is this," I wonder, studying my two guests, who are looking at me with a smile. "When did they get here?" I try to make out in my mind. "Um, help me, now what's your name?" I ask the young lady and the man. "I am Chris, your son-in-law and this is Kathy, your granddaughter. We drove you here yesterday, remember?" Chris tells me. I couldn't say that I remember and I don't understand what they mean with driving me here, but I play along. "Oh, yes, the house is getting along nicely, isn't it? I like this room, its not that crowded," I gesture around the room. "It is, it's very comfortable and bright," the young lady joins in and smiles. She reminds me of someone. "What's your name?" I ask her. "I am Kathy, your granddaughter," she explains. "Oh, yes, of course you are," I lie, hoping she doesn't notice. "And where do you live?" I carry on. "We both live in Switzerland. Do you remember Switzerland? You used to visit us a lot there," she asks me. Switzerland does ring a bell and while I think of it I feel it's a place I like a lot. "Switzerland, yes, I was in Switzerland. That is a beautiful place, isn't it?" I reply, feeling more comfortable. I know that I know that place and felt comfortable there. Having this little piece of memory makes me feel happy but sad at the same time. Happy as I am proud of being able to link the name, and sad because I cannot remember more clearly. I feel I am missing pieces of myself and though Switzerland has a beautiful ring to it, it also awakens sadness inside of me. Something happened in Switzerland that makes me feel uneasy, so much I know. My eyes water unexplainably. I sniff, and try to swallow down the knot in my throat with another sip of tea. With an automatic movement I fish out a handkerchief that is held by my wristwatch and dab my eyes. I am a little surprised, if I would have thought about how I can find a handkerchief, I wouldn't have known. But this seems to be an automatic movement, stored as a daily routine. I don't feel I have too many of these left. "It's a very nice place, you loved the mountain flowers," the young lady awakens me out of my thoughts. "Um, I do love flowers, we will need to get some gardening done here soon," I reply and study her face. She reminds me of someone. "I had a daughter once, I think. She was in Switzerland, you know," I say watching her face and feeling confused by my own words. "Yes, you did, that's Mum, Sue, remember?" Her eyes are suddenly sparkling as she asks me. "Yes, but it's long ago. Where do you live?" I ask trying to change the topic as I feel I won't be able to keep up answering more questions. "We live in Switzerland," she explains and the sparkle in her eyes dies down.

The days go by quickly, and I have no clue what day of the week it is, let alone the month. The seasons pass by, and for a moment they let me realize the time of the year. Years are passing without me noticing. Only my birthday cakes remind me that another year has passed. The carers tell me my age, but I have forgotten it again at the next moment and I definitely don't have enough fingers to count, trying to figure it out. It doesn't bother me and therefore doesn't really matter. I am comfortable and have made a new friend called Mary. I don't always remember her name, but that isn't important. I have cleverly got used to getting through the day without having to use names.

Anyway, I think I am doing quite well with my situation and I don't think many people notice my missing memories. Only now and then I get very frustrated and angry. That's when words that I don't know come out, words that I had stored inside of me.

Mary and I like to sit together in one of our sitting rooms and watch the garden. "Oh look, Mary, the gardener is here," I tell her in excitement. I love it when the baker comes in the morning, and now and then the gardener in the afternoons. The attention I sometimes get goes down like honey and sweetens my soul. "What are they doing here? They will be asking for enormous amounts of money again. And for what? For cutting back some rose bushes. My husband can do that. Can you call Abigail? We got to tell her to stop them," Mary nervously complains. "Abigail.

Abigail," she shouts and presses her handbag tightly to her body. "They're not getting my money," she grumbles. I agree with her when it comes to the money part. But, on the other hand, I do like to see the young men and maybe get a smile from them. I wouldn't want to miss that.

Abigail walks over, strokes Mary's back and leans down to her. "Mary, darling, what's the matter," she asks with a kind voice. "There," Mary points out to the garden. "They are here again. I'm not going to pay for them. Tell them to go, my husband does that," she orders with a strict tone. Abigail sits down on the couch armrest and keeps on stroking Mary's shoulder. "Don't worry, love, they do a good job of the garden and we will take care of the bill," she tries to calm her. "But not with my money," Mary hisses back, she is clearly not calmed. "What's the time?" She asks Abigail. "It's 3.30 pm. Would you ladies like a drink?" Abigail kindly asks us. I nod with a happy smile. Abigail is such a nice person, I think. "Okay, I will get you both something refreshing," Abigail promises, stands up and vanishes into the kitchen. Mary has started to search her handbag. "My son will be home soon. I need to get home and start making dinner," she grumbles, while picking out every piece in her handbag. "Will he?" I ask a little absently, looking out into the garden. "Yes, he is home from work at 5 p.m. I want to have dinner ready for him," she carries on picking out more items. "I can't find my key. Do you know where I have it?" She asks, getting more and more nervous. "I am sure it's in there somewhere. Have you looked properly?" I ask, turning my attention to her handbag. Abigail is back with two glasses of orange squash. "Here we go, ladies," she says, placing the glasses down on the coffee table in front of us and winks. "What's the time?" Mary barks at Abigail. "Um, it's 3:35 p.m.," Abigail calmly replies, looking down at her watch. "I can't find my key. Do you have it?" Mary carries on complaining. "Love, you don't need your key. Everything is safe. Your son, Peter, will be here tomorrow to visit you," Abigail explains, before leaving to attend another patient. "Oh," Mary mutters and her facial expression relaxes a little. She closes her handbag and we both lean back into the couch and enjoy our orange squash.

Five minutes later, Mary starts rummaging in her handbag again. "Do you know where my key is?" She asks me. "I'm sure it's in there somewhere," I reply, gesturing to her handbag. "My son will be home soon from work. I want to have dinner ready for him," she explains, getting more and more nervous. "You will be okay, don't worry, it'll be there somewhere," I try to calm her. "Abigail. Abigail," Mary shouts, seeing her pass by at the other end of the room. "Yes, love?" Abigail patiently asks. "I can't find my key. Do you have it?" Mary complains. "My son will be home soon, I have to make sure he gets his dinner," she says, explaining her distress. "Love, your son Peter will be here to visit tomorrow. You don't need to make dinner for him today. All is fine," Abigail calms the situation. "I don't know," Mary grumbles, and carries on picking her handbag up and down. I know she feels ready to go, but she doesn't know where to go or how to start.

We sit here on the couch until dinner and the scenes repeat themselves, but we don't mind. We don't notice.

CHAPTER TWENTY-FIVE

I'm sitting alone in an armchair. Mary isn't here anymore. The nurses told me she was not well and that they had to take her to hospital. I don't remember exactly what was wrong and I can't sort out the days or weeks that she has been gone. It feels like a long time ago and my memories of her are fading. Even though there has been quite some attention around me this week, I feel lonely. I wish my time was up and that I could leave too.

Barbara has been here. She visits me often and I can remember her name on good days. Stuck in thoughts that I cannot even recognize, I sit and stare holes into the air. I don't notice three people walking up to me, and jump at hearing Abigail's voice. "Mollie, you have visitors from Switzerland. Your granddaughter and her husband are here," she beams at me. Behind her, a young lady and a fair man are nervously bobbing from one foot to the other. "Why don't you two sit down here next to her," Abigail offers. After hugging me, they happily sit down and the young lady fiddles with her fingers. "How are you, Nana?" she asks with a soft voice. "Oh, I'm fine, thank you. You know, the same old me. There is always something to do around here,"

I smile, and wonder exactly who she is. I feel comfortable and close. That tells me they must be family. "Well, you look good, Nana. Look, we have brought you some photographs of our wedding," she pulls some glossy pictures out of a white envelope and stretches them towards me. I take the pictures and study the first one. The young lady and the fair man on the picture are dressed-up looking smart. She is wearing a long white dress and veil that is invisibly pinned to her beautifully combed hair. He is in a black suit with white tie and handkerchief sticking out of his blazer pocket. A cream-coloured rose is fastened to his jacket buttonhole. "They both do look elegant, don't they?" I say, gazing at the pictures. "It was a wonderful day. We were really lucky with the weather," she brightly smiles. "This is Andreas," she says, gently laying her hand on the fair man's arm next to her. "He is the groom on the picture," she explains. "Oh now, you could charm any duck off the pond looking like that," I chuckle. Andreas laughs sincerely. His smile warms my heart and I cannot help but return his smile. "Where was this?" I ask. "It's Switzerland. We got married in Switzerland," my granddaughter quickly replies. "Yes, I know Switzerland. I was there a long time ago," I tell them, feeling proud to remember the place. "Now, your name is?" I ask the young lady. "I'm Kathy and this is Andreas," she gestures to the fair man next to her. "Do you have children?" I ask. "No, we don't," she replies. "I had a child once, but that's long ago," I tell them both. "You did, Sue, my Mum," she smiles at me. "Hmm, yes, I did," my thoughts wander, and I feel sad as I stare out into the garden. Not knowing what to say further, I start to whistle a tune that takes me back to my childhood memories. I didn't even know that I could whistle, and I quite enjoy this distraction. The melody fills the gap, sounds happy and I don't need to think of what I am expected to say. Both Kathy and Andreas are staring at me with their mouths open. "The garden is looking really nice," Kathy finally says, finding her voice again. "It is. It takes a lot of work though. I am always out there doing something," I explain, not feeling sure if my words are true or not. I remember I had a garden, but I'm not sure if it's this one or not. "You know, we have rebuilt this place quite a bit. It didn't used to be like this," I explain. Both look a little astonished and I wonder if I have said something silly. Maybe I should have just carried on whistling. For a moment I don't feel myself, my tummy is feeling off. Every now and then such a wave of pain rushes through me, making me clutch my tummy and try to press against the stinging feeling. But I don't want them to leave. Their company feels good, and I'm happy to have someone next to me. "You can keep the pictures. We have put some notes on the back, our names and such," Kathy smiles. "And we have given the nurse a nice bottle of sherry for you," she winks. "Sherry. That will be nice. I enjoy a glass before I go to bed," I explain, feeling excited and automatically start to whistle again. "Oh, your nails are nice," Kathy notices and takes my hand into hers. I don't know what she means and have to study my fingers before answering. My nails have a pretty pale pink, shiny colour. I cannot remember where I got this from, but I guess it must have been one of the nurses. Or maybe it was the hairdresser, I think, and feel the tips of my hair to see how they sit. They feel well groomed, so I decide to go with this variation. "The hairdresser did them. I do like it, it's a lovely colour," I explain and stretch both hands in front of me to show off the vanish. "They are, and they match to your clothes," the lady admiringly acknowledges.

"Now, you will have to help me, what's your name?" I ask, realising I have two young people in front of me. "I am your granddaughter, Kathy and this is Andreas, my husband," Kathy explains with a smile. A new wave of pain shoots through me and I feel a little pale. "Are you all right, Nana?" Kathy asks me, noticing the brief freezing of my face. "Nothing to worry about," I reply and rub my tummy. Abigail is back with some tea and biscuits. "Mollie is having some pain in her abdomen area. The doctor will be here tomorrow and will check her," she explains, noticing my guests' worried expressions. "The doctor. An examination," shoots through my mind. "Over my dead body. No strange men are examining me," I decide for myself, and give Abigail a non-appreciative look.

After we have enjoyed our tea and chatted for a while, Kathy starts to get jumpy. "We better get going," she tells Andreas. They both smile at me and a feeling of sadness creeps up on me. "We have some chocolates for you." Kathy bends down and fetches a neat little box out of her bag. "They are the nice ones from Switzerland." She hands me the box and then stands up and hugs me. "Take care, Nana. I love you," she kisses me on the cheek. Andreas follows and gives me a warm hug. They both stand and look a little unsure. "Well, we will see you again soon," Kathy nervously smiles and looks down to the floor. My eyes water, I cannot help it and I don't understand what is going on with me. I mean, I can't even remember who these people are. But my heart is touched and I would like to be able to leave with them.

"Why is everybody always leaving and I am always staying," I ask myself, and swallow the thick knot in my throat. Kathy and Andreas turn at the door and wave one more time. A salty drop falls from my eye down onto the box of chocolates that is resting on my lap. Trying to distract myself from the upcoming emotions, I desperately try to open the boxes silky, navy-blue ribbon. The knot is firmly tied and my fingers are too large to loosen the single threads. Frustrated, I sit back and let my tears fall. "I cannot even open this damn box of chocolates," I cry to myself, feeling angry with the world.

The doctor comes the next day. After my bath, Sophie, the morning nurse, takes me to a small examination room on the first floor. Sitting on the fixed stretcher doesn't make me feel comfortable and I am tired. The last nights haven't been good. The constantly recurring pain had made it difficult to go to sleep. I had woken up several times during the night, and had ended up crouched together in a little ball, waiting for the morning to come.

A knock on the door startles me. "Hello, Sophie," a bald-headed man in a white jacket sticks his head into the room. "Hi, Dr Andrews, come in," Sophie smiles, and makes space for the doctor to enter the room. "Hello, Mollie," the doctor stretches out his hand towards me. "Good morning, doctor," I unwillingly respond, and shake his hand. "I have been told you're having pain in your abdomen area?" He asks me. "It's not that bad," I lie, and wrap my arms around me in a protecting way. "Do you mind me examining you?" He asks with a sympathetic smile. "Yes, I do mind! I don't want to be examined by you or anybody else. I am not taking off any of my clothes," I firmly state. "That will make it difficult to diagnose the pain and find the right treatment for you, Mollie. I do insist, we must examine the area of pain," Dr Andrews looks worried, while I feel pressurised and trapped in a corner. Like a little wounded bird that cannot fly. Shooed into a dead-end corner by a hungry cat. Anger takes over. "No! No you're not, you hairless person. I am not having any of you examine me," I fiercely shout. Dr Andrews and Sophie stand in front of me with their mouths open. Sophie finally finds her voice. "Mollie, Dr Andrews only wants to help. Are you sure you don't want to accept? I'll stay with you, I promise," she begs me. "It's alright, Sophie," Dr Andrew calms her. "Mollie, do you mind if I just scan your tummy? You can leave your clothes on." Both are goggling at me, waiting for my next move. Slowly I unwrap my arms and hold them on each side of me. Dr Andrews gently taps my tummy without any further words. "Hmm, it's difficult to say. You could have a tumour that's causing the problem. If that's the case it's serious, and an operation would be necessary." He ends his scan. "Your age and your unwillingness to be examined are not in favour of such a step," he carries on, and makes some notes on a pad. "Here we go, this is a prescription for some medication that will help relieve the pain," he says, handing a leaflet to Sophie. "There's not much more I can do, I'm afraid." He looks at Sophie with a serious expression. "If there's any change of the situation, please call me," he kindly offers. "Mollie," he stretches out his hand to shake mine.

The pain keeps on growing even though I am receiving Dr Andrews' medication. I don't spend much time out of bed. Movement is too disturbing for me. I spend much more of my time in darkness for myself. Day for day, I start to ignore the carers running around me trying to persuade me to take a few bites or have some water. I just don't want to anymore. This is the chance I have been waiting for. My chance to leave, my time to go and nobody's going to take this from me. It surprises me that I am able to hang on to this decision so well, and be persistent about it over days. The thought is so clear, like a crisp wind that swipes you across your face and takes away all obstacles that are in your mind's way. Suddenly, all is clear and you wonder to yourself why it took so long to find this special thought. For me, the crisp wind, or in my case the pain growing in my abdomen area, takes away the difficulty of having this clear thought. My decision against my body's will to overcome this sickness is strong, unbreakably strong, and it relieves me to know that I will soon be going home to my dearly missed loved ones.

But I had underestimated Abigail. She is in my room every day with breakfast, lunch and dinner. This morning, Sophie is with her once again. "Mollie, dear, you need a wash and change of clothes. There will be no backing out of this!" Abigail explains with calm voice. I can feel her tugging the blanket that is warming me. "Go away, will you. I'm fine. Why don't you people just let me sleep," I complain without opening my eyes. Abigail tugs one last time and the warm blanket flies away, leaving me curled in my nighty. I grumble loudly and turn onto my side. "Okay, I am going to assist Sophie, dear. Now don't worry, all is fine," They both carefully lift my nighty up over my head. This is embarrassing, I think to myself and feel furious. "How dare you do this," I shout at them as loud as I can and, in the same moment, jump as I feel a smooth, damp sponge clean my leg. "We will be finished in a minute and you can get dressed. You have a visitor today, you know," Abigail informs me while gently washing the other side of me. "A visitor, who could this be," I wonder to myself while scanning both ladies above me. "Your grandson David is coming all the way from Switzerland to see you, dear," Abigail softly winks at me. "David" shoots through my mind. My grandson, I should be able to remember this, I think. But the clouds have not been swept away from this part of my mind. Half an hour later, I'm dressed in one of my pretty skirts and cardigans. Sophie chose some matching pearls for me and forced me to sit upwards in my room's armchair. "Don't you want to take a bite?" Sophie asks me, looking down at the thin sandwich they made me. I just glare at her to make her leave the room and take a sip of the tea they have brought. "You don't want to fall asleep when your grandson is here now, do you," Sophie warns me, before turning to leave. Leaning back into the chair, I enjoy the warm feeling of the cup of tea in my hand, and let my thoughts go blank.

"Mollie, dear, David is here to see you," Abigail's voice wakes me. I have no idea how long I had been sitting, or let's say sleeping, here. The cup of tea in my hand has gone cold, but I don't mind, I wasn't intending to drink it anyway. "I will help you get up. David is in the other sitting room." Abigail reaches for my arm. To have to move disturbs me terribly and doesn't fit in with my plan. "I just want to lie in the darkness for myself. Why does nobody understand," I swear inwardly, and feel Abigail's hands firmly clutch beneath both of my arms and slowly start to lift me. "Put me down! I'm not going anywhere. What am I doing out of bed anyway. How dare you do this," I shout at her, but she doesn't stop her mission. Instead, another young female carer comes to help her. I don't recognize this young lady. Her dark hair is combed to a ponytail and a dark fringe surrounds her hazelnut eyes. A black ribbon with bow is tied around her small head just above the fringe. "And who are you anyway," I shout at her. "What do you think you look like with this black thing in your hair? You look like a beetle. Now put me down," I carry on, swearing at the top of my voice. The young lady looks at me with widened eyes, full of horror, and then shyly looks over to Abigail. For a minute Abigail freezes, but it doesn't take a second and she bursts out into laughter. "Don't worry, Sara, this is our Mollie," she tries to explain between coughing laughter.

Up on my feet, I feel more self-dependent but Abigail doesn't let me go. "Now I'm going to walk with you, Mollie. You haven't been eating for some days, so you might feel a little dizzy." Feeling furious, I let her guide me to one of the small sitting rooms. A young couple is sitting on the sofa. The young man immediately jumps up as I enter the room and walks towards me. "Nana, it's so great to see you.

Happy Birthday," he smiles and embraces me. Holding on to Abigail's arm, I have no choice but to let him. It flatters me to be hugged by a young man and I have to giggle while Abigail carefully sits me down in an armchair. The words he said somehow don't arrive at my brain. Two young people with big brown eyes are happily smiling at me from the sofa. I am not sure what to say. "Do I know these two? What did they say?" I wonder to myself. They do feel familiar, but I cannot place them.

"Mollie, dear, I will leave you with your grandson, David, for a while. Okay? I will be back soon with some refreshments for your all, right?" Abigail bends down and strokes my shoulder before leaving the three of us. "Oh, yes," I reply, watching her walk out of the room. "Now, did she just say their names?" I try to recap the last seconds, but nothing comes to my mind. I feel exhausted and only want to get back into bed. But, on the other hand, I have these two wonderful people in front of me to whom I feel attached and don't want to miss. Not knowing what to say, I just whistle, my new answer to all situations that I feel stuck in. The young man smiles heartily and his eyes twinkle with joy. "Nana, do you remember who I am?" He asks me, and stretches out his hand to hold mine. Here we go. How am I getting out of this, I think to myself. It's just getting too tiring. "You're family aren't you?" I ask back. The young man looks excited. "Yes, we are," he beams. "I'm David, your grandson and this is Joya, my girlfriend," he gestures to the young lady sitting quietly next to him. She smiles at me and shyly looks over to David. "The carers told us that you are not well," he carries on. "I hope you are feeling better," he asks with widened eyes.

"Oh, well you know. I'm fine, just a little tired," I answer, choosing the easy way out. "That's good to hear, I'm sure you can have a rest later on. I mean, it's your birthday and you should be fit for later. Surely you will be having a little party and a cake, right?" He expectantly smiles at me. "Birthday? Cake?" I repeat in my mind, feeling confused. "Ha, ha, I just cannot keep up with my age nowadays. I don't have enough fingers to count," I laugh, going with the story. "We will be having a party later. Nothing big, you know, just some cake for all," I add, feeling pleased with myself. "You're 96 today, Nana. What an age!" He informs me, looking proud. "I am 96," I tell myself, and for a second wonder where all these years have gone. "Yes, I must be," I agree and start to whistle again.

After tea and cake, David and Joya decide to leave, but promise to be back tomorrow.

The cake uplifted my spirits, and I decide to eat a few bites, as I didn't want them getting suspicious. Having something in my tummy once again makes me feel better and more alive. As they will be back tomorrow and it's my birthday, I decide to also have dinner. I want to stay in a good shape for my family's visit.

CHAPTER TWENTY-SIX

I lost my short, uplifting moment a few days after my grandson, David, and his girlfriend left. I had been out of bed some hours a day and managed little portions of food and drink. But the waves of pain don't get less. On the contrary, they get stronger and the time intervals between shorter. My thoughts are focused back on letting the demons take me this time. I don't want to fight, this is my time, this is my journey. Day for day, the hours of being out of bed reduce. If Abigail or Sophie get me up, I put up with the process of being washed and dressed. As soon as they sit me down in an armchair, I close my eyes and quietly fall asleep. My dreams are full of pain that I consciously ignore. All my remaining energy is focused. They are not going to soften me up and persuade me to do this or that, to enlarge my time on this planet. "I'm leaving. I'm leaving," I mumble, not caring if anybody can hear. Finally, the carers give up trying to get me up and let me rest in bed. Now and then they come and wash me, change my nighty and swamp my mouth with a damp, bitter-tasting, giant cotton wool stick. I have lost orientation of days and nights, and rarely open my eyes. The only channel to the outside world is the calm voices of the carers who come and read stories to me, play my favourite music on a small CD player and Barbara, who softly speaks to me. She tells me of my life, my family and how the garden is looking. I like to hear her voice. Over all these years she has been my angel functioning in the background, pulling the right strings and making sure I am okay. I am endlessly grateful to have her to rely on if worst comes to worst, even if it means putting up with her inspections.

As my mind comes to peace, my thoughts become clearer and I can take in the words that are softly spoken to me. They let me dream for a moment, relive a scene and remember my loved ones and favourite spots. Not eating or drinking is tiring me out terribly though, and my moments of concentration do not last.

And then they are there again. My enemies of the past and now allies of the future who will pave my path. I can hear their laughing echoing through the darkness. "Mollie, dear Mollie," a croaky voice whispers and is followed by an unhealthy cough. The thing clears its voice. I am lying on my bed. Everything is dark around me, and I cannot see a thing. I try to lift myself up, but I am weak and a gluey texture is pinning me down to the bed. Managing to lift my arm, I can see the black glue pulling threads that eventually give in and rip apart. The leftovers dangle from my arm like pieces of seaweed hanging from a net. A foul smell surrounds me and strengthens with every outward breath the creature takes. It must be somewhere close to my head as I can feel its breath brushing the side of my face. "Yes, Mollie, yes I am. I will stay close. Close," it laughs, and I can feel its sticky long fingers comb my hair back out of my face. Its pointy nails scratch my forehead, and I try to move my head out of its touch. A wave of pain runs through me. Groaning, I lay my freed-up hand on my stomach to try and sooth the root. "It takes time. Time," the creature explains. "We are many, but you are strong. Very strong. But we have time. We are patient," it laughs, and I can hear the words echo off the walls around me. There is movement in the room. I can hear rustling noises coming from beneath me. Now and then I believe I can see little flashes of light from my enemies' eyes. Frantically, I try to lift my other arm from the bed. The texture is heavy and thick. It costs me all my remaining energy to free my other arm, and it immediately drops down onto the bed after the sticky strips that were holding me down have ripped. Panting I lie there, and know I am at mercy of this awful creature. The thing just sits there and whistles a croaky tune. But its melody quickly quietens and I can feel its head moving from one side to the other. It is distracted by something else. A soft breeze slowly makes its way into the room, taking away the thick, hot air. The feeling is welcoming to me, but not to the enemy. It snorts loudly and pulls its fingers away from my hair. "Mollie, dear Mollie, we will be back, you will see," it coughs, and I can feel it move backwards, away from me. I try to lift my arm again, but I still cannot find any energy left inside me. The air clears and the room lightens to a soft colour. The foul smell evaporates within seconds. A gentle hand wraps around mine and I can feel a thumb stroking across my fingers. A fine delicate energy has filled the room. At the same time it is sad, and my heart is pulled in two directions. A thick wet drop falls onto the back of my hand. I can hear a male sob escape the lips of my visitor. A head with soft hair buries itself next to my arm and weeps. I can feel his body trembling next to mine. I feel so sorry that I cannot take him into my arms. A strong energy attaches us, and I know we must be close family. A tear escapes my eye and runs down my cheek, and finally dries between my skin and the cushion. The moment between we two is so intimate and peaceful and yet I know that this young man is scarred and full of deep sadness. A sadness that is very familiar to me, and I know we share the same thing. The man stays with me the whole day, and I am so grateful that we can share these moments together and exchange our deepest wounds without words. This will be our last meeting in this world. But I know he is one that I will always stay with, wherever I am.

The room's energy around us suddenly strengthens. It's as if the air could be ripped apart. A cold shower runs down my back, and I feel icy breath exhaling from my body. A smooth, silky cloud surrounds me and my dearly missed daughter's voice whispers to me. "It's Matthew, your grandson Matthew," I can feel a light touch of soft skin brush mine, a touch of heaven. I feel so happy and protected. It's as if the highest mountaintops of love are touching my soul. The feeling that I had missed so much is suddenly here, surrounding me with love and comfort. I smile and rub the side of my face against the cushion. The silky cloud suddenly starts to move away from me and panic of losing her again shoots through my veins. "Have trust. Have trust. We will never leave you," I hear the heavenly whispering of my daughter in the distance.

Matthew is still lying beside me and seems to have calmed. We stay like this until I fall into a peaceful sleep.

When I awaken he is gone, and I feel we have said our farewells.

The next days I am drawn back and forth into the dark world of the demons that surround me. They are brushing texture onto my skin. The foul smell burns my nostrils but I cannot move to escape their work. While they go on painting my skin, they hum melodies that I too had whistled a few weeks ago. "We were there. We were there. We learn and work quickly," the broken voice proudly whispers to me. Its breath makes my tummy turn. Seeing me choke makes the thing laugh. Its companions join in and the evil sound echoes through the room. My stomach feels like it is boiling, the heat that arises is unbearable. Pressing my chin down to my chest, I am able to glimpse down at my body. The creatures have pilled green mass all over my abdomen area. Bubbles are growing. The green skin is stretching itself and fills with air, and then sinks down again only to rise up a second later. Every time the bubbles reach their full size, my tummy stretches and it feels as if I would burst any minute. "Not much longer. Not much longer," the voice whispers.

I cannot hold my head any longer and sink back down into the pillow and squeeze my eyes closed. "If only they would get it done with and let me go," I pray, and hear laughter close to my ear that ends in a snarling sound, like dogs that are shooed into a corner. Once again the room lightens and the bad smell is replaced by a fresh flowery scent. I can hear voices speaking calmly. Abigail is explaining something to some people. She comes closer and strokes my arm. "Mollie, dear, you have visitors. Barbara, Chris, your son-in-law, and Kathy, your granddaughter are here," she gently whispers. "Take a seat wherever you feel comfortable. You can stay as long as you want. I'm afraid she isn't opening her eyes anymore and she hardly speaks. Please let me know if you need anything, wont you?" I hear her telling my guests before leaving the room. "Barbara, Chris and Kathy," I repeat this in my mind and feel at peace. The three stay with me the whole day.

Chris tells me his exciting stories about his new dog and the times we had together. I love to hear about animals and the thoughts make me smile. Kathy is on the other side of my bed and holds my hand. She doesn't say much, but I enjoy feeling her calm presence. My long-missed family is in the room, joining me on my last path. The thought is soothing. But I cannot help the choking feeling arising stronger and stronger inside of me. My stomach is boiling.

Towards the evening, after Barbara had left, I cannot hold back anymore. The pressing feeling is overpowering. My tummy lifts and my skin is stretched to its limit, until it cannot take anymore. Deep down inside I can feel something burst. For a second the tension is gone, and my tummy sinks down again. An unbelievable pain shoots through me and for a moment I fall into unconsciousness, only to be wakened a second later by an upcoming rush of boiling fluid that is finding its space by darting up my gullet. I cough, and splatter dark red blood onto the blanket covering me. Around me the room immediately awakens, and panic breaks out. I can feel Chris and Kathy jumping into action and helping me to lean over. "Kathy, pull the emergency cord," Chris orders and lays his arm further around me for support. More blood pours out, down the sides of my mouth and onto my nighty. I can hear Kathy rush to the front of the room. A siren sounds, and two carers are in the room within seconds. They lay a towel around me. "It's okay, dear, it's okay," Sophie calms me. "Make sure you get it all out. That's a good girl," she strokes my back. "Abigail, we need the ambulance," she shouts to the room's entrance. "Chris, Kathy, you can wait in the sitting room. The ambulance will be here any minute," Sophie carries on giving orders.

Hours seem to pass by, that are more likely only minutes, while I carry on coughing and splattering. I can hear the echoing of dirty laughter in the distance. "It's done, it's done," my enemy proudly whispers for only me to hear. "Here we go. Here we go," they joyfully sing around me. Their whispers quieten and are drowned by the high pitch sound of an ambulance siren outside the house.

The pain of my opened inside is overwhelming, but the thought of my ending somehow calms me and comforts my soul. "This is it. This is my time," I repeat in my mind like a mantra.

Within seconds my room is bustling. Two emergency doctors check me while my carers change the blankets and clean me. In the distance, I can hear the doctors and the carers speaking to each other, saying that there is nothing much they can do. They inject something into my arm, but I hardly realize. I am already on my path. "We want to keep her here if that's okay. She knows us and we can support her best. We don't want her alone in some hospital bed," Abigail distinctively determines. I smile, realizing her words, and feel at rest knowing I can make my journey in a surrounding of people I love and who care.

As soon as my room has calmed and all is cleaned, Chris and Kathy come back beside me. Barbara has also returned, and the three of them just sit and listen to my favourite music.

In my world, the bubbling fluid has died down and is voicelessly covering my skin. I can feel the sticky texture dry on my skin. It pulls together as if I was covered in clay that is drying in the sun. A fresh wind pulls through the room and brushes the surface. I know it's not going to take long until all will crumble and I will go with it. But I want to hang on. I want to go through this moment by myself. My moment of leaving shall only be mine, and I want to feel free in these steps.

Kathy is sitting on the corner of my bed and is gently stroking my hair. It feels heavenly to feel her touch. She is strong, and I feel I can share my thoughts with her. I believe she can hear my plea to let me take my last steps alone. She bends down and gently kisses my forehead. I know she is going to leave, and I try to smile to thank her. "Be on with you," I manage to mumble and I feel her smiling down to me. Her love touches me, and we are sharing the thought that I will soon be home. Home with my loved ones. I know that she knows this, and that she looks forward for me. "Good night, Nana," she whispers and touches my hand a last time before standing up and leaving the room. Chris and Barbara also say their goodbyes, and I say my farewells to them without speaking. It is wonderfully peaceful and I feel my part on this earth is truly done. I have said farewell to all that matter to me here, and feel blessed to have had this possibility.

Once they have left I fall into a deep peaceful sleep. I don't know how long I stayed resting in this position, waiting for the next phase. A damp swamp moisturising my mouth awakes me from my deep sleep. I can feel Abigail move through the room and sit down in an armchair. Peacefully I inhale and exhale. The atmosphere around me starts to change. The room's energy heightens. It feels like just before a summer storm. I am back in my world. The dry clay around me cracks and deep scars open up and push themselves apart. My room has lightened and the curtains are drawn back. The hatch holding the window closed opens by the building pressure. Fresh air blows into the room and the white delicate curtains play in the breeze. Their silky surface touches me and the clay starts to crumble, freeing my body. A sharp gush of wind blows through the window and sweeps away the clay's dust. The fine powder rises to the sky and plays in the wind. I realize my body has crumbled with the clay. I am part of the dust swirling around in the air.

Looking down to the room I was in, I see Abigail looking up from the book she is reading. As she looks at the bed, the book in her hand drops onto her lap and her left hand presses against her heart. Tears run down her cheeks and I know she has witnessed my passing. In my mind I say farewell, and thank her for her years of support and love. I close my eyes, deeply inhale and stretch my arms to the sky. All pain has gone, I am free. I am dust swirling around into the sky accompanied by heavenly tunes. Letting go of all I have carried for so many years, I enjoy the feeling of lightness. All thoughts are gone, there is no yesterday nor tomorrow. There is only the now.

The wind carrying me dies down and I believe I can feel something beneath my feet. Opening my eyes, I look around. I am standing in a lane. On both sides are small houses with rose bushes in front. But there are no colours. All is brownish, as if I would have fell into an old sepia-toned picture. Looking down at myself I realize I am back in my body. But I am young, my hands have no wrinkles and I am wearing my favourite flowered dress. Carefully, I take a step. My body moves lightly without a sound. Smiling for myself, I make a few steps and twirl once on my tiptoes. "Yes, I can do this," I joyfully sing and watch stardust jump into the air every time I move.

A short distance away, I hear a door open and close. A gate squeaks. I look in front, and spot two people walking out of a house onto the lane. Suddenly I realize. I know this lane and I know the cottage the two people came out of. This is my home lane, my cottage. Standing still, I watch the two people. Standing next to the cottage gate, they stop and turn towards me. Both of them smile and wave. Swallowing deeply I know who is standing in front of me, welcoming me home. With tears of joy running down my face, I start to run towards them. Bill and Sue, my second husband and my only child, open their arms to greet me and I let myself fall into their embrace. Together we hold each other, laugh and cry. I have no questions. I am home, just home, where I dearly wanted to be most. The feeling and the touch I missed so dreadfully are real again. They hadn't forgotten or left me after so many years. They were always here, patiently waiting for me. Waiting for us to be reunited.

The wind around us picks up. We are lifted up from the ground and I can feel us swirling into each other towards the sky together. The breeze carries us as we melt together and scatter across the land.

We are dust, beautiful stardust, with a lifetime in between that has finally found home.

We can shed tears that she is gone
or we can smile because she has lived.

By an unknown author

Epilogue

Dear Reader

'From Dust to Dust and a Lifetime in Between' is inspired by a true story. Mary Eileen Cooke, or Mollie as her family and friends called her, was born and raised in a small English town and lived most of her life in Church Stretton, close to the Welsh border. She experienced both World Wars, the 1st as a child seeing her father going off to war and coming home with the rank of a captain. During the 2nd World War, both her brothers served in the Royal Air Force, and she sadly lost her first husband. Fortunately enough, she fell in love again, and married William Henry Cooke (or just known as Bill). At this point in life everything seemed to fall into place, and she was blessed with a beautiful daughter whom she loved more than life itself. She never got over losing her to cancer, and it troubled her that she couldn't take her place. Her daughter, Susan Mary Lee, left behind three young children and her husband.

Cancer came back into Mollie's life when she lost her dearly loved husband. Due to her traumatic experiences with this illness, it was an important part of the book to give cancer a face, and to investigate how such a creature, if you can call it this, could look and act.

Mollie, my grandmother, again and again expressed her wish to write down her story, but sadly her dementia did not give her the time to do this herself. "Who knows what I could get up to as just a "flat line"?" Well, this book shows what Nana could be up to. I thank you, Nana, for spending so many months with me in spirit and letting me write your story. You will never be forgotten, and your story will now live on forever.

In the name of Mollie and our family, I would like to thank Barbara Bengry, her niece, from the bottom of our hearts for taking care of her and for always being there. The Hartland's Rest Home in Abbey Foregate, Shrewsbury, took care of Mollie during her last 6 years of life. The love and care that Mollie experienced there can never be expressed enough, and I thank all the staff dearly for always being with her and accompanying her on her last journey. We will never forget.

Katherine Anne Lee